Spiritual Sugar

The Divine Ingredients to Heal Yourself With Love

Lisa Manyon

Spiritual Sugar: The Divine Ingredients to Heal Yourself With Love
by Lisa Manyon

ISBN: 978-0-9822950-0-7 (softcover)
       978-0-9822950-1-4 (ebook)
       978-0-9822950-2-1 (hardcover)

LCCN: 2022921064

Advanced Praise

"Spiritual Sugar is a powerful testimony to the healing power of love! When we say yes, as Lisa did, to allowing love instead of fear to be our sacred navigation system — miracles unfold. *Spiritual Sugar* is an inspiring must-read for all who desire to embrace their spirituality and intuition in a much deeper way!"
~ **Linda Joy,** Publisher of *Aspire Magazine*, Mindset Mojo™ Mentor and Bestselling Publisher

"This book is the tale of a journey: a journey into love, healing, and growth. Lisa shares what she has learned from her experiences of growth and healing — and acts as a guide as she offers insights and practices that can aid you on your own journey. *Spiritual Sugar* ... it's sweet, but it's the good-for-you kind of sweet. Because maybe the world has had enough of the old belief that healing has to be a hard, bitter road. Maybe it's time to embrace what's possible using what Lisa shares in this book and let your life get sweeter, richer, and better than ever before."
~ **Jacob Nordby,** Author of *The Creative Cure* and *Blessed are the Weird*

"Once you've navigated a life-threatening personal crisis that ends up bringing profound change and healing, you KNOW how to support others. That's why *Spiritual Sugar's* time has come! In Lisa's magical yet practical new book, not only does she share a multitude of ways you can access the same Divine love and healing SHE tapped into, but also the kind of wisdom that only comes from walking through the fire. Life threw me similar challenges years ago, and I believe, as Lisa does, these experiences come to wake you, not break you. Whether you're struggling emotionally, physically, or spiritually, this loving and insightful guide will show you how to awaken to your powerful inner resources,

gain clarity, and peace of mind, and start to heal on all levels. 'Spiritual Sugar' is the L♥VE you've been looking for. I highly recommend it!"
~ **Lisa Winston,** Intuitive Artist, #1 Best-Selling Author, Inspirational Speaker, and TV Show Host

"I've known Lisa for many years and her heart has always been her biggest asset. Her willingness to concentrate on the positive, and do everything with L♥VE has truly inspired me, especially as she was on her cancer journey. *Spiritual Sugar — The Divine Ingredients to Heal Yourself With Love* should be read by anyone and everyone who needs to embrace their self-care and self-love."
~ **Tracey Ehman,** International Bestselling Author, Podcast Host of Silver Lining Conversations

"Lisa's incredible journey reveals the pathway for you to tap into the sweetness of your life. She takes you by the hand and offers a roadmap for you to heal, transform and LIVE your best and sweetest life. Dive in, enjoy and get ready to experience your unique, miraculous life."
~ **Wendy Darling,** Miraculous Living Institute and author of *Create Your Miraculous Life — It's NEVER Too Late*

"*Spiritual Sugar* brings to the forefront a powerful reminder that Love is the essence and energy that heals all. With emotion, honesty and transparency, Lisa shares her personal journey that carves a path so you too can reclaim your power to Heal With Love. This book holds the vibrational knowledge that inspires healing on all levels. Grab your journal and get ready for transformation! *Spiritual Sugar* is a must-have book you will return to for comfort, guidance and inspired growth for you and for all of humanity."
~ **Rev. Marilyn Rodriguez,** #1 International Best-Selling Author, Leading Spiritual Healer, Sovereign Self-love Mentor

"In *Spiritual Sugar,* Lisa shares her personal journey of healing with love to release cancer including alternate healing modalities to complement Western Medicine. I've used many of these throughout my own healing journey when diagnosed with stage 4 breast cancer and given 90 days to live. Lisa and I have both walked this path and collaborate to share resources with the world. *Spiritual Sugar* is written so beautifully with such love, and Lisa provides resources for you to consider to fortify your well-being. Everyone needs support, resources, and a touch point when facing mortality. Spiritual Sugar sparks hope for all of us."
~ **Michelle Patterson,** Touchpointe, Inc. CEO and Founder

"*Spiritual Sugar* is a testament to healing yourself with love and aligning with your spirituality. Lisa teaches that when we cleanse our mind, body and emotions, we access our innate power and connect with our soul's highest potential. She gives amazing journal prompts about self, health, and wealth that ask the deeper questions intended to preempt a major crisis and be courageous and present. This book helps one to understand what it means to have full ownership and responsibility for where we are now, and tapping into the sweetness of life, and love yourself NOW."
~ **Nicole Doherty Ananda,** Life + Relationship Coach

"This book is good for the soul! Lisa's journey is one of courage, faith, and is deeply inspirational. Her story of overcoming cancer by understanding how to heal it with love is one that we all can benefit from, and this book will deepen your connection with your Source."
~ **Therese Skelly,** author of *Love Based-Mission: How to Create a Business That Serves Your Life*

Dedication

*To my birth family, soul family, sacred sphere of influence,
the amazing medical professionals at OHSU and
Oregon Ear, Nose & Throat Center, and God. Thank you for
BEing. I couldn't have done any of this without YOU!*

*May you question everything,
challenge the status quo,
break the trance and engage in critical thinking.*

*Here's to tapping into the inner sweetness of your soul,
coming home to yourself and healing with L♥VE.*

*With special remembrance and reverence for Viki Winterton.
Thank you for being such a beautiful soul. Fly with the angels.*

***Quick disclaimer: Throughout this book, I'll share lifestyle, health and wellness tips but I'm not a doctor. My suggestions work for me. I'm sharing a personal experience and this should not replace what you're doing with your own health-care professionals. Every ailment, every cancer, and every person is different, and we must do our own due diligence to find the best healing path for ourselves. This information is intended to help empower YOU to make the best choice for you so you can redefine your relationship with SELF, HEALTH, and WEALTH and deepen your spiritual connection. It's highly recommended that you seek professional therapy to navigate any challenges that arise while working through the exercises, **Spiritual Sugar Heart Sparks** journal prompts and information in this book.

Foreword

Anybody who has survived cancer is worth listening to.

They may have an insight, a method, a therapy, an alternative, maybe even — dare I say it? — a cure.

That's why this book is crucial. Too many people are suffering. Too many people are giving up. Too many people are dying.

Yet there is another way.

A way to health and healing, wellness and radiance, and even to love and freedom.

Lisa has been there. She got cancer. She healed herself of cancer. She's now sharing her story, her insights, and her love.

Spiritual Sugar is all about healing with L♥VE. That's what I love about it. We all know the world needs more healing. It needs more love. We've heard it and said it a hundred thousand times. But how many of us are living and breathing it?

Lisa shares her personal journey with cancer, her connection to the Divine, and many alternative healing modalities. You should consider her suggestions when you commit to healing yourself of anything. Lisa's been there. She knows. She can help.

In essence, Spiritual Sugar is about tapping into the inner sweetness of your soul. It's about coming home to yourself to heal yourself with L♥VE.

It doesn't matter if you (or a loved one) face cancer, some other disease or challenge, or whether you have a migraine, back pain, or daily distress.

The answer is the same.

Shower yourself with love.

Lisa will show you the way.

Follow her wisdom and then —

Expect Miracles!

~ Dr. Joe Vitale
http://www.MrFire.com

Dr. Joe Vitale is the globally famous author of way too many books to list here, from *The Attractor Factor* and *Karmic Marketing* to *Zero Limits* and *The Miracle*. He is a star in the hit movie, *The Secret*. He hosts the popular weekly online TV show, *Zero Limits Living*. http://www.ZeroLimitsLivingTV.com

Table of Contents

The Spiritual Sugar Experience is a Journey of Awakening

Have you ever thought you had it all dialed in? And then something shook your world to the core? My deepest spiritual awakening was highly personal and came in the form of facing mortality. In 2017, my life changed forever. You might say this was my moment of awakening although previously I thought I was pretty tapped in. When I was faced with mortality, I acquired a new understanding, and I knew it was time to get serious about healing with L♥VE. Coming home to myself took the form of a serious medical diagnosis. For many, coming home falls into at least one of three categories.

1) **Self**: This means you face some kind of existential crisis. You begin to question everything you had previously believed. The focus here usually involves faith, values, and what matters most. This is the place where you reset your relationship with YOU.

2) **Health**: This means you experience a health crisis. Something wakes you up and requires change. The focus here usually involves your mental, physical, and spiritual well-being. It's the space where you redefine your relationship with your mind and body. And, you realize you have one body and one life (at least this time around).

3) **Wealth**: This means your relationship with money changes in some way. This is where you examine what wealth means to you. It could be that you've been impacted by an

unexpected emergency. Maybe it's time to get serious and build your nest egg to let money work for you? Or you finally realize that money is a tool to provide more freedom. This is the place where you tap into the energy of money to better support you. The focus here involves taking a deep look at how you interact with money, your fiscal responsibility, and potential. It is important to remember that this goes deeper than money. Your journey of coming home to yourself will be unique to you.

As you navigate the changes required to redefine the relationship with Self, Health, and Wealth, you'll find that you're embarking on the greatest personal evolution of all time.

Your life will change.

The people you surround yourself with will change.

Your faith will deepen in ways you've never imagined. You will come home to yourself.

It is my sincere wish that you have the support you require to redefine your relationship with Self, Health, and Wealth before you experience a wake-up call. Following are some journal prompts to begin your journey of healing with L♥VE. You'll find additional prompts throughout the book. Let's go deeper! Welcome home! ♥

Journal Prompts,
Also Known As
Spiritual Sugar Heart Sparks

Throughout the book, you will find **Spiritual Sugar Heart Sparks**. These are journal prompts to help you go deeper. I recommend that you set aside some sacred time to move through the exercises. This will be most impactful when you have a dedicated journal and set a timer for a minimum of five minutes for each exercise.

With that being said, this book is designed for YOU to choose the divine ingredients to heal yourself with L♥VE. Move through it as you are guided to. There will be sections that draw you and that deeply resonate with your soul. Pay close attention to these sections. There are divine messages and activations that you will uncover here. On the flip side, there will be sections that are uncomfortable and that you don't want to look at. Pause and look deeper. This is the deeper inner work that is calling your soul.

As you grow and evolve as a person, going deeper to redefine your relationship with Self, Health, and Wealth is a big part of your spiritual awakening. These journal prompts, **Spiritual Sugar Heart Sparks**, are designed to help you identify what matters most.

1) What is the most important thing in my life right now?

_____

_____

_____

_____

2) How am I connected to my faith? (In other words, what do you believe in and how do you strengthen that connection with your Higher Power)

_____

_____

_____

_____

_____

3) Am I pausing to love and honor myself? (What have you done for YOU lately?)

_____

_____

_____

_____

_____

4) What is my relationship with my health? (Are you eating well, exercising, taking mental health days, etc.?)

_____

_____

_____

_____

_____

5) Do I have a healthy relationship with money? (Are you building wealth and letting money work for you?)

_____

_____

_____

_____

_____

♥   ♥   ♥

I recommend investing in a paper journal and a nice pen to go even deeper and record your thoughts. Visit https://SpiritualSugar.com to order a Spiritual Sugar Journal. A thought becomes a bright idea, and when put in writing, words turn ideas into action.

This Book Is For YOU

While the majority of my work is designed to support women, I know this book will find its way into the hands of many wonderful men too. I trust that the message will be received as intended and ignite more love in the world.

This book is for YOU. The little you who knew your magic was connected to something bigger, deeper and more purposeful than most people can imagine. This book is for the you that you were before the world told you who to be.

Pause for a moment and think about that. There is great power in the pause. Sometimes we have to slow down to speed up and that reminds me of a saying inspired by the Navy Seals, "Slow is smooth, and smooth is fast." So, pause now, take a deep breath and tap into the center of YOU. You might want to grab a journal and your favorite pen for this experience because I am going to ask you to do some inner work. And you are invited to write in this book. You have full permission to make this your own. Doodle, make notes and do the exercises as you move through the process of embodying yourself. Let your inner child roam free as you navigate this process. Some of the material in this book may bring up deep emotions for you. I highly recommend enlisting the support of a professional therapist to move through any areas that require further thought, support and attention. The only way out is in and through.

I invite you to grab a cup of tea or your favorite beverage, settle in and set a timer for five minutes.

Answer this question: *Who were you before the world told you who to be? I mean really, at your core*, what were your deepest desires and what fueled you to BE?

_____

_____

_____

_____

_____

It's quite possible that you were brave, fearless, uninhibited, full of wonder and curiosity, and then life happened. Your reprogramming began. Reprogramming based on family, community, religion, the school system, the government, and even your own fears and doubts. You began to question you. To forget the true magic of your uniqueness. You likely stopped being love, giving love, and receiving love freely. The love that you are was overridden by programming and now it's your time to reclaim your sacred essence.

You've likely heard this saying, "Children should be seen and not heard." This is a Victorian-based idea that obedient, quiet children are superior to other children. Interestingly enough, it originally applied specifically to young women.

With history like this, it's not surprising that the societal and generational impact of specific sayings like "It's not polite to brag" and rhetorical questions like, "Who do you think you are?" continue to hold back women even today. It's hard to imagine a time when keeping to yourself was seen as a superior quality. You were not designed to shrink. You were designed to learn, grow, expand, flourish and be the best version of yourself. This requires owning your magic and reclaiming your God-given birthright as you strip away everything that no longer serves you.

Fast-forward to present day, and you'll see that many people still find themselves bound by the invisible chains of antiquated thinking and even familial programming. You may shrink, retreat, hold back and perhaps you don't speak up and share what's on your mind. It's quite possible that you are subconsciously afraid, maybe because you were taught as a child that bragging isn't polite or you simply don't want to outshine your peers because you might crave acceptance. The possibilities are endless, but the fact

8

remains the same: Each of us is born with a unique gift. Your particular gift or talent might be similar to others' but it cannot be fully duplicated because it is uniquely yours. To take it a step further, it's paramount that you accept that you are meant to share your gift with the world. When you don't, without realizing it, you actually do a disservice to the world. There is only one YOU and the world is waiting for you to be all you're destined to be. Often, in order to embrace your gifts fully, you must heal parts of yourself that are yearning to be reclaimed and recognized.

Our unique gifts are meant to help people truly make a difference and to evolve our planet in a positive way. Understanding this, the antiquated beliefs of history, society, friends and even family become less impactful. Knowledge is empowering. When we know in our hearts we are meant to make a difference, we owe it to ourselves and our fellow humans to step forward and be heard. More women are choosing to express these gifts by starting a business, becoming an entrepreneur, or sharing their stories (this isn't exclusive to women, of course, and at the same time, women have been silenced throughout history and this is shifting). We create new opportunities as a conduit to share our gifts by providing services and benefits for the greater good. We have the power to share our gifts in many ways, and one of the most important ways is by letting people know how our unique gift can benefit them. This is where the challenge of overcoming those old-fashioned negative thoughts begins.

When you feel your gift with your heart and soul, you know you are doing the right thing. Your gift may simply be BEING you because that is enough. Yet, at times, those ingrained, limiting beliefs can creep in and hold you hostage. You probably feel the gifts, you want to share the gifts and yet there is likely a niggling feeling of guilt, shame or fear. So, how do you overcome this? How do you move past the uncomfortable feeling of sharing your gifts with the world? It all begins with your inner game. This means the way you feel about yourself, and the work you do to make a difference in the world. It is also the personal practices you develop to be more tapped into your higher self and source. The more you own your gifts and support yourself, the more you can contribute to humanity and support others. This is true both in your professional and personal lives. Often, before you can step into a place of confidence to fully express yourself and BE who you were meant to be, you have to step back and look at what has caused resistance from the inside out. You can do this by making a list of your gifts and how they can help others. This will help you identify where your personal power has been diminished by programming. From there, it's important to embrace those gifts and own the responsibility of sharing (after all, if you don't tell, who will know?).

As you tap back into who you are, take inventory of your gifts. Here are some **Spiritual Sugar Heart Sparks** to consider:

1) Make a list of your gifts and how they help others (no gift is too big or too small — even a smile is a gift to the right person).
2) Embrace your gifts, reclaim your personal power, and accept responsibility for sharing (Write the poem, paint the picture, do THE thing).
3) Share your gifts from a place of service and love and your message will flow (What do you really want the world to know about you?).
4) If you're still stuck, consider creating a practice to tap into the essence of YOU (Think about what lights your soul on fire and brings you deep satisfaction and do more of that).
5) Keep a journal of success and celebrate your wins (big and small, celebrate it all).

_____

_____

_____

_____

_____

By being aware of who you truly are and how the gifts that you possess impact the world, you're one step closer to coming home to you and to healing yourself with love.

With this newfound clarity, you'll discover even more ways to help more people and make the difference you know you are meant to make.

So, this book is for you. Your inner child who needs more love and is ready to be fully seen and heard. The child who longed to be received with open hearts and arms and to be told what a special, sacred being you truly are. Here's to cleansing your mind, body (your sacred temple) and soul to align with your highest calling in life. Sometimes that calling is to do less and be more.

Imagine if we were all taught to BE exactly who we were designed to be from the very beginning. Imagine being told how wonderful, beautiful, unique and special each human is and being shown that your body truly is a sacred temple. Imagine how the power of this knowledge could have sparked a divine truth within you to ignite a passion for living, caring for yourself and creating healthy boundaries from the beginning.

This book is about spirituality, not religion. Spirituality and religion are two different modalities. Spirituality is what your soul is conveying to you; religion is what someone else is telling you.

Spirituality is about healing with L♥VE on all levels and embodies:

- Tapping into Spiritual Sugar: the inner sweetness of your soul
- Coming home to yourself
- A deeper connection with Source, God, and your Higher Power (whichever term you prefer)
- An undeniable connection to nature as proof there is something bigger than US
- Tapping into your intuition and higher self for clarity and direction

And most of all the book is designed to ignite your passion for life and help you develop practices to give yourself the love you deserve.

There's going to be a time in your life where you start questioning everything especially spirituality and religion. This might be that time. You may be called to or away from a certain path. You may begin to explore many different beliefs.

Inevitably you will find your way home to yourself and your connection to something greater than YOU.

Nature has always spoken to me. When I was a child, I spent a lot of time outside with imaginary and not so imaginary friends. As I grew up, there were times when I lost that connection. And while it's important to go inward to clear the cobwebs of your mind to move forward, sometimes going outside is exactly what is needed to get clear on what's going on inside.

In short, don't let the world tell you who to be. Consider these **Spiritual Sugar Heart Sparks** and take five minutes to answer these questions.

- How old were you when you first started not wanting to be who you were?
- Was that your choice?
- Or the influence of others?

_____

_____

_____

_____

_____

Preface

"I was told to challenge every spiritual teacher,
every world leader to utter the one sentence that no religion,
no political party, and no nation on the face of the earth
will dare utter: 'Ours is not a better way,
ours is merely another way.'"
~ Neale Donald Walsch

I've been a seeker on a spiritual journey for as long as I can remember. And the journey has been mine.

Raised by two loving parents who were both disillusioned and traumatized by the Catholic School system, religion and spirituality were not table topics. My Godmother (some traditions carried over including my christening in the Catholic Church — I still have my gown) shared her sage wisdom that "God is dog spelled backwards." So, I explored my relationship with the spiritual world, God and the miraculous energies of the Universe on my own.

I learned interesting lessons along the way. Like when I was in preschool or maybe Kindergarten and we went to Ohio to visit family. I went to school with a distant cousin and clearly felt out of place in the structured religious confines, especially when I was chastised for taking a bite of a cookie before prayer. I simply didn't know what I didn't know.

What I did know is there was a power much bigger than ME in the world, my imaginary friends were not imaginary, and my 6th sense was always on overdrive. But I hid it because I knew I didn't fit in and what I experienced was not what everyone else around me was experiencing. Plus, when I spoke of it, people didn't believe me... or simply thought I had an overactive imagination.

For a time, I dabbled in the Baptist religion and for the span of a year or so when I was 12, I attended church on Sunday learning

Bible verses and eventually being baptized in the flowing waters of The Mattole River between Petrolia and Honeydew, California.

> *"For God so loved the world that he gave*
> *his only begotten son so that*
> *whosoever believeth in him shall have*
> *ever lasting life."*
> ~ John 3:16

When I moved to Lewiston, Idaho, I attended a couple of different congregations for a stint but none of them stuck. I felt the confines of organized religion to be too stifling for me. Yes, I felt a direct connection with God, I still do, and I know in my heart there is most certainly something greater than us at play in our world. I don't believe this is God alone. I believe God is a part of it and so is the energy of our world, Universal principles, and the absolute power of nature. All of the spiritual and religious teachers of our world, Jesus, Gandhi, Buddha, you name it, are sources of wisdom that we can all draw from and as long as the focus is positive, there is room for everyone. This led me to study many different beliefs including the Hebrew Tree of Life principles. My journey as a seeker continues and I'm always fascinated by how faith and a strong belief in God (insert whatever term you're most comfortable with) bind the tapestry of humanity with commonality (even those who don't believe).

I honor your beliefs no matter what they are. I personally believe there is something much bigger than all of us and I like to learn about the different religious and spiritual practices throughout the world.

Exposing yourself to different beliefs is essential to growing as a person. It's also very helpful to know there is a force much bigger than any of us and sometimes it's important to "let go and let God" (or insert the deity of your choice here).

I've discovered that if I'm focusing too much on the "how," it's time to let go and give universal laws some time to start working for me. Spiritual growth takes many forms and it's up to you to discover what works best for you and truly feeds your soul. For me, nature brings me closer to divinity.

My best tip for spiritual growth: Don't be afraid to pray. Sometimes even that small act can make a huge difference. If you're not comfortable praying, try meditation or a walk in nature.

A friend once asked me what I think "God" is… I answered, *"I don't know for sure but what I do know is it's a greater power than me, I feel it deeply, I have faith that there is something bigger than me, I feel the energy, and I believe the love of God starts from within."*

Today, this is what I know. Everything I do is divinely driven. When I get off track, I get major God Nudges and sometimes they shake me to places and experiences I have never imagined.

My most recent journey brought me to Ashland, Oregon, where I feel more at home than I've ever felt anywhere. On occasion, I attend services at the Unity church but for the most part, I get my connection to God from nature, meditation, and prayer.

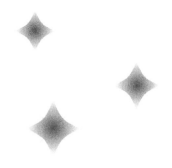

SECTION 1

The Awakening

CHAPTER ONE

Shaken, Not Stirred

How I ended up in Ashland, Oregon

The road home is long and winding. And home is wherever YOU are. I lived in Lewiston, Idaho for twenty years and never really felt like I belonged. Although, to be fair, it wasn't necessarily the geography that made me feel that way. It's how I've always felt for as long as I can remember.

I knew I needed a change but I didn't know exactly what I needed. Years before I visited Ashland, I receive an intuitive message (often referred to as a download) that told me to move to Ashland. I ignored it. And, as you'll find while I share various experiences throughout this book, when you ignore the God Nudges you receive, you will be shaken to where you need to be and not always in the most graceful way. When you ignore the initial stirrings of divine direction, be prepared to be shaken to where you're meant to be. Shaken, not stirred. When you pay attention, you can avoid a major disruption and instead follow the inspired flow.

It takes courage to do many things in life because we fear the unknown and we fear failure. How many times in your life have you wanted something, REALLY wanted something, but didn't act because you were afraid of the consequences? You lacked the courage to follow through for yourself.

Courage comes in all shapes and sizes. This is, in part, because your fears are unique and individual to you. Much like snowflakes, no two people are exactly alike. Therefore, your motivations, fears and the level of courage you display are not something that can be compared or even measured. Courage is a personal journey and one worth exploring.

Courage often means change and this is where things can get really uncomfortable. Although you may realize that the only thing constant in life is change, it's human nature to be drawn to the familiar. The familiar keeps you safe, the familiar gives a sense of security (often falsely) and the familiar can often keep you stuck in the status quo (without you even realizing it). You probably notice that you crave the familiar because it feels safe and at the same time the familiar keeps you in a holding pattern — you stay where you are to avoid risks. Because taking risks means you could lose or fail. That's the fear talking. In reality, by not finding your inner courage, you are actually failing yourself. Taking risks can mean wild success but it takes courage to see that, even more courage to take action and extreme dedication to move forward.

This quote by Raymond Lindquist spoke to me, *"Courage is the power to let go of the familiar."* This is true and yet too often you might not exercise this power and take action to create the life you truly dream of.

When you become courageous and push past the familiar, it can be extremely uncomfortable and absolutely exhilarating. Yes, there are unknowns. There is fear. There is a bit of an upheaval. Sometimes a big upheaval depending on the level of courage and change being called forth. The size of the upheaval means an even bigger uplevel. You may have heard about the breakdown before the breakthrough and you may have experienced this yourself.

When I finally embraced courage and decided to go to an unfamiliar place in Ashland, Oregon for an extended stay in a magic writer's cottage to create the life and work I really wanted to share in the world, it was a huge leap of faith. The journey was both scary and exciting. During the process of making this BIG move, I noticed the one thing that had been holding me back was fear. It's also likely what holds you back.

There were several questions I asked myself when making this decision to embrace change, be courageous and do something different.

These **Spiritual Sugar Heart Sparks** may help you find the courage you need to do what you really want or need to do. Set your timer for at least five minutes and explore:

1) Why am I fearful of this change?

It's important to know the root of your fear. Is it a gut feeling based on intuition that could protect you or is it the kind of fear that gives us butterflies of excitement and uncertainty right before we step out of our comfort zone?

There is a fine line between our intuitive senses and the brief uncomfortable period that comes right before change. It's important to trust your intuition and gut feelings and to know when it's really time to be courageous. I examine and embrace my fear to determine if it is intuition kicking in to warn of a choice that isn't my best interest or if the fear is just the normal, excited, scary fear that comes right before I make BIG change and am going to move forward.

_____

_____

_____

_____

2) Will this change result in creating the life I ultimately desire?

It's important to make choices that are in your best interest. All too often our choices are made based on external factors. Carefully weigh why you're making changes.

One thing I knew for sure is that I'd always wanted to explore somewhere new and to make a move based solely on what is best for me. It felt a little selfish (leaving friends, family, my home and more) but I knew in my heart I needed to find the courage to make the move or I would stay STUCK.

_____

_____

_____

_____

3) Does this feel right to me?

A simple way to determine the right choice to make is to really notice if it feels right. Chances are if it feels right, it's the right thing to do.

This goes back to intuition and honoring what is our highest good. I carefully weighed all options and knew in my soul of souls and heart of hearts I had to make the change no matter what. It took a lot of trust, faith and immediate action. I had to summon great courage.

_____

_____

_____

_____

When I chose to move to Ashland, I secured a magic writer's cottage for six months to explore what was working and what wasn't working in my life. I took the time and the courage to examine what I really wanted in life. I took daily action to move towards my dreams. And it was scary sometimes. And exciting sometimes. Life is an adventure waiting to happen if you choose to explore and play. Do I know what's going to happen next? No, but I do know I'm exactly where I need to be to design a life that fully supports me. And I believe this divinely orchestrated move saved my life in more ways than one. When the six-month stay in the magic writer's cottage was complete, I knew I wanted to say in Ashland. I manifested a condo and traveled back to Idaho to get my belongings. I drove a 17-foot U-Haul 640 plus miles from Idaho to Oregon solo and I've been here ever since.

As I focus inward and get really clear on the changes I want to make in my life and business, a passage from the book, *Turning Pro*[12] by Steven Pressfield is fresh in my mind.

"The professional displays courage, not only in the roles she embraces (which invariably scare the hell out of her) or the sacrifices she makes (of time, love, family) or even in the enduring of criticism, blame, envy, and lack of understanding, but above all in the confronting of her own doubts and demons."

When you embrace courage, not everyone will understand. You'll have to let go of some things, some people and some plans. But ultimately, the only person you need to honor is yourself. Without truly honoring yourself, you cannot fully engage with life, L♥VE or the passion of creating your magic in the world. Do you have the courage to do what it's going to take to succeed?

As the great Walt Disney once said, *"All our dreams can come true, if we have the courage to pursue them."*

CHAPTER TWO

Enter Spiritual Sugar... (The Backstory)

While sitting in my office in Ashland, Oregon, seemingly out of the blue, I received a clear message that I am to write a book titled Spiritual Sugar and that it will be about healing with L♥VE. Getting a divine download or God Nudge like this isn't new to me and at the same time, this one was unsettling, stretchy, and, honestly beyond my comprehension at the time. After all, I was already fulfilling a God-given purpose to teach marketing with integrity with a focus on PASSION Points through my business, Write On Creative. The message to write the book came through loud and clear and I felt like it was too big for me and that I'm not the expert on the topic and every other excuse you might imagine when God gives you yet another BIG mission.

This happened on August 28, 2015. I journaled about it, scribbling down the words "Spiritual Sugar" and "Give Yourself Some L♥ve." I wondered why I was being charged with speaking/

writing about healing with L♥VE and tucked that divine charge away in my journal. I also had a major "Who am I?" moment as I pondered why I was being given this mission to write about this topic (and I found, that when you don't listen, divine downloads and God Nudges will knock even harder). A month prior to this newest suggestion, I had written in my journal: "*I feel a gentle calm within that is guided by a restless willfulness. What does that even mean? It means change is coming and the deepest most personal growth I have ever experienced is on the horizon. I am looking forward to seeing what is next.*"

My intuition was knocking even before God knocked. I've learned to listen deeply and follow the threads. I was deeply craving the feeling of fully being in my body and optimizing my health. I knew this needed to be a priority and I wasn't quite sure what my next steps were.

It was also in August of 2015 that I received a download (aka God Nudge) that it would be in the highest to attend a *Conversations with God*[13] discussion group. Mind you, I had never read the books and was somewhat surprised to receive this divine direction. I discovered a local conversation hosted by Neale Donald Walsch himself. For several Tuesday evenings, I attended this gathering to BE present. To listen. To learn. To familiarize myself with the material in his books. At the end of one of the sessions, Neale gifted all attendees a pass to one of his spiritual retreats. I gratefully and graciously accepted and spent three days receiving beautiful wisdom and sharing community with the group.

This was my first retreat with Neale and I'm still impacted by the magnitude of this amazing gift. I have never before attended an event where such love and care were given freely and purposely to ensure everyone was OK on every level. The CWG team deserves many kudos and thanks. During the event, I witnessed Neale's love, commitment, integrity, and humanness. I found the experience to be unparalleled. I am honored and blessed beyond belief to have been a part of the magic AND it was magic (my mind is officially blown). Three statements Neale made are prominent in my mind today.

1) *"YOU are worthy because YOU are."*

2) *"Understanding replaces forgiveness in the mind of the master."*

3) *"It is the nature of humans to try to talk others out of happiness."*

Fast-forward to 2017. As I usually do each year, I set a theme or essence word(s) for the year. This is what I wrote in my journal on January 1, 2017.

1/1/17: *"I awoke to fresh snow. The pathway of a new start. My essence word(s) and focus for the new year…*
Whole-being Wealth.
This is multi-layered intention that permeates all areas of my life including health, wealth and happiness. It also incorporates core principles of legacy, leadership, and luxury.
As a whole, many of us take for granted what is right in front of us. Being focused encourages us to embrace the moment and think about the future, the wealth of our LIVES, our communities, and our world. Cheers to Whole-Being Wealth. May we live it, breathe it, share it and keep it."

Little did I know how poignant this journal entry would be. As I rolled into 2017 with hope and optimism, something was clearly amiss. In February, I began to feel off. I had a cold that took a while to shake. I started taking my health more seriously. Joined Weight Watchers and soldiered on.

In March, I scheduled a video shoot to create an online training for Write On Creative. I wasn't feeling well the day of production. My throat was scratchy and I thought I was just resisting doing the videos (being on video is not my first love). I hired Neale's son, Nick Walsch for videography and it was all I could do to get through the day of shooting. Although the con-tent is excellent, when I watch those videos now, I can see how sick I really was.

I had reached technical obesity and was carrying 189 lbs. on my 5'7" frame. While I carried it well, I was not well. I went to the see my health-care practitioner to share with her that I was still experiencing symptoms including a scratchy throat, a lump in my throat that I felt each time I swallowed. My throat also burned and I was experiencing pain in my chest in the form of what felt like massive pressure. I was told it was probably an abscessed tooth. I was prescribed antibiotics, and I flew to Los Angeles for a business conference and to visit with friends and family.

While in LA, my friend Lisa and I went for a Champagne hike at Terranea Resort as one does while in Rancho Palos Verdes. As we were walking, she noticed I was out of breath and we hadn't even truly exerted ourselves. I confided in her and told her I hadn't been feeling well and that I knew something was seriously wrong but I didn't know what it was.

The truth is, I felt as though I might not live. I didn't utter those words to anyone else, but when I boarded the plane to go visit, I had this little thought in the back of my mind that I might not have much time left on the planet. I chose to go on the trip anyway because I wanted to have all of those experiences no matter what happened... the hike with a longtime friend, time with my aunt and cousin, and beautiful gathering of souls at a business conference. Regardless of what was in store for me, I knew it would be OK, life or death. After all, that is the circle of life.

When I returned to Ashland, Oregon, I scheduled a meeting with my health-care practitioner and shared a slew of additional symptoms that had surfaced while on the antibiotics and on my trip. She immediately wanted to prescribe me an acid reflux rem-edy and I was livid. I wanted answers about the root cause. I felt the lump in my throat growing and it was beginning to cut off my airway. She kept asking me what I thought it was, and I had no idea. Finally, she asked me if I thought it, was cancer. WTF! Are you serious? Why would she ask me that and how would I know? A little thing like never going to medical school precluded me from being an expert in this particular area. My intuition told me something was off but never in a million years did I think it was cancer. I knew at that point I clearly needed a new doctor and a referral to an Ear, Nose and Throat specialist.

On April 27, 2017, when my friend Shana and I arrived at the ENT, the stop sign out front of the facility was upside down. That felt quite fitting for the roller coaster ride I had already been on. The visit to the ENT confirmed that I had a growth in my throat. What started as a tickle in late March had grown to over 2 centimeters big (that's a bit over an inch and around the size of a small walnut).

AND that is when my journey really began. On May 5th, I celebrated Cinco de Mayo by having a biopsy. Shortly after that, I received a cancer diagnosis that changed my life. I knew in that moment the only choice was to heal with L♥VE. I leaned deeply into my faith, I followed the divine threads to the healing modalities that would best support me and complement Western medicine. And I knew in my heart of hearts and soul of souls that chemo and radiation were not a path I would choose. There were tears, of course. I knew this was a huge choice point and it was up to me to save my life, reclaim my health and trust without a doubt that the only possible outcome was healing with L♥VE.

Spiritual Sugar™ invites us to re-examine who we are, how we show up in the world, and what we truly want to experience in life by taking full ownership and responsibility for where we are now. It's about tapping into the sweetness of your soul and being fully present in your life.

My goal is to share tips, tools, and TRUTH that you can apply to your life no matter what your situation. By making some of the shifts I'll share, my hope is that YOU can avoid cancer altogether by living a healthier lifestyle. If you are impacted personally by cancer or are a caregiver, you can start healing with L♥VE by taking action and putting yourself and your health first.

Come inside as I share my journey of healing with L♥VE and sprinkle a little Spiritual Sugar™ on your life to tap into:

- Faith in the power of your mind, body, soul, and conviction to heal with L♥VE.

- Curiosity to question everything and push beyond the perceived limits.

- Self-Care to strengthen yourself, your personal desires, and your connection to your Higher Power.

- Health to boost your immune systems with pure food, clean water, and natural healing techniques.

- Wealth to feel the inner richness that we are all afforded in this life and to master the ability to create security for yourself.

This is about keeping it real, being okay with not knowing what's next, and living in the moment. It's about redefining what matters most and how to go deeper to take better care of yourself. As I share my healing journey, my wish for you is that you select ingredients that resonate with you and that YOU can apply to live a healthier life.

In our lifetime, 1 in 2 people will be diagnosed with cancer. In this case, it was me.

However, I refused to let that define me and I didn't ever claim the disease as my own. Instead, I focused on making positive changes. AND I'd love for you to do that NOW before you get a serious wake-up call.

An Overview of The Journey

In a nutshell, I was divinely guided to heal cancer with L♥VE and this is where I share my experiences with YOU.

From intuitively knowing something was "off"...

- to being asked, *"Do YOU think you have cancer?"*...

- to a divine download with the guidance *"You will heal this with L♥VE"*...

- to wondering *"Am I being delusional? Am I going to die tomorrow?"*...

- to having absolute faith that whatever was meant to be would be...

- to keeping the journey quiet and within the sacred sphere of influence to ensure optimal healing...

- to being told *"you won't be able to work for at least 2 weeks,"* which in reality was a lot longer...

- to realizing that a three-month financial cushion is never enough for a real emergency (hence a focus on wealth and in wealth-building, not just making money) ...

- to navigating two surgeries fearlessly (no matter the outcome) ...

- to discovering life-altering information about how cancer is being treated...

- to dropping 40 lbs. in under one year (no weird diets, just real food) ...

- to quitting my four favorite food groups cold turkey — a miracle in and of itself (coffee, wine, chocolate, and cheese) ... Not to mention eliminating all processed sugars

- to tapping into spirituality, guidance, and intuition in a much deeper way than ever before

- to embracing a completely new lifestyle (with WAY more self-care and energy healing modalities included).

CHAPTER THREE

My WHY for Spiritual Sugar

There is always a WHY behind every mission. As with most things I do in life, the Spiritual Sugar mission is divinely inspired and continues to be guided in this way.

The Spiritual Sugar mission is simple yet complex, "Heal Yourself With L♥VE."

I get a lot of questions about Spiritual Sugar and my healing with L♥VE journey... So, I thought I'd address them here and share a bit about my WHY.

When I received the cancer diagnosis, I kept it quiet. I shared with my sacred sphere of influence and focused on my faith and healing with L♥VE. You may not know me and may be just learning about the cancer diagnosis and what I've faced. Although I have a rather public persona via my speaking and work with Write On Creative, I am a very private person. So, if you do know me and the cancer journey is new to you, that's because I made a conscious choice NOT to plaster my journey all over social media (although I know many of you would have sent love and support or wanted to know what you could do to help). I was guided to navigate this with grace and dignity to demonstrate another way to approach such jarring news. I had to focus on my **SELF**. Quite frankly, it was a matter of life or death.

I made a conscious choice to heal with L♥VE (thanks to some very clear God Nudges). I eliminated all processed foods, eliminated sugar, started juicing and more. I made sure taking care of me was the #1 priority and committed to a bunch of other powerful changes to reclaim my life. I had to focus on my **HEALTH.**

I made a conscious choice to NOT create a Go-Fund-Me page to ask for support. Again, I chose to keep what I was going through quiet and relied on close friends and family to help me through. I did create a private PostHope[32] page to share with my sacred sphere of influence but I didn't ask for money. Some might say this was ego-based and they could be partially right — It's not easy to ask for help — especially monetarily. Hence, the focus on **WEALTH**. AND I am here to tell you that the three-month cushion we're advised to amass in case of an emergency — doesn't scratch the surface of a real emergency.

However, I felt in my heart of hearts that my faith would pull me through (and I continued to run my business — business as usual minus not being able to work for a while). This also brought me to a humble place where I can share my journey, be fully transparent and inspire others to do the same.

Spiritual Sugar is growing organically. I share my healing with L♥VE journey to inspire those of you who wish to take control of YOUR life with a focus on SELF, HEALTH, and WEALTH before you're faced with a health crisis. Also, to give you thrivers, who've supplemented traditional and Western medicine with other natural, healing modalities, a platform to share your stories to help others understand that it is possible to heal with L♥VE.

But let me be perfectly clear, Spiritual Sugar is not about cancer. Cancer was the catalyst to help me complete this and reset my life. I am not qualified to consult about cancer because each cancer is as unique as the individual who experiences it. What I did worked for me but it might not work for you. That being said, we can all take measures NOW to heal ourselves with L♥VE, live a healthier lifestyle on many levels, and hopefully avoid a startling wakeup call, like a diagnosis of cancer. I can share divine ingredients that I used to heal with L♥VE AND then you can consider the information to create your own recipe.

Here's WHY I'm doing what I'm doing.

Remember when I told you that two years prior to receiving a cancer diagnosis, I received a divine download that I was to write a book called *Spiritual Sugar*? I didn't immediately act on this request from High. As a result, I was shaken into the journey of healing with L♥VE. I was also divinely guided to share with you that Spiritual Sugar is not a religious movement. The Creator shared with me that too many people have lost faith due to the misuse of organized religion and the overall state of our world. I have been asked to lead you home to yourself by helping you focus on SELF, HEALTH, and WEALTH — but beyond that to get back to basics. Meaning to tap into nature. The message I received is that when people have lost faith or hope, it's important to spend time in nature to reground, look around and be reminded that nature is a clear sign there is something bigger than ourselves at play. I'm also told that spending time in nature is the best way to get a direct connection to your higher self and God. Basically, we need more love, faith and nature in our lives.

The intention is to focus on healing with L♥VE and redefine your relationship with SELF, HEALTH, and WEALTH. This is also a global platform to share stories of healing from thrivers to promote hope and help others avoid a wakeup call (that usually comes in the form of a health crisis like cancer).

Each year on World Cancer Day, I am thankful for life. I am thankful for my medical team (primary care, ENT, and surgeon). I am especially grateful for those who focus on energy healing, homeopathic applications, naturopathic remedies, integrative, and functional medicine. I honor those who have walked this path and been involved in educating the public about alternative ways to elevate personal wellness and complement Western medicine instead of pink-washing* everything while not really doing anything.

To each of YOU, my Spiritual Sugar friends, I encourage you to take charge of your health and focus on clean eating (study nutrition, your doctor isn't an expert in this — that's why they've chosen specific specialties and they are very good at staying in their own lane). We are responsible for our own health and we must do our due diligence to determine what fuels health and what causes illness.

AND above all else, I encourage you to focus on healing with L♥VE instead of "battling," "fighting," or "conquering" anything. Words have energy; intentions have energy. What we say impacts how we heal and what we do determines how well we will live.

There will be more to come. For now, if you'd like to be a part of this evolving journey, you can choose to do so by visiting http://www.SpiritualSugar.com.

Let's sprinkle a little Spiritual Sugar on your life and watch the miracles unfold!

*If you're not familiar with "pink washing," do a little digging and be sure the causes you support are truly supporting the causes they claim to be.

CHAPTER FOUR

Spiritual Sugar Values

Achievement of your happiness is the only
moral purpose of your life,
and that happiness, not pain or mindless self-indulgence,
is the proof of your moral integrity, since it is the proof
and the result of your loyalty to the
achievement of your values."
~ Ayn Rand

The core values of Spiritual Sugar include:

- **Faith** *in the power of our mind, body and soul, and conviction to heal with L♥VE.*
- **Curiosity** *to question everything and push beyond the perceived limits with intuition.*
- **Self-Care** *to strengthen ourselves, our personal desires, and our connection to our Higher Power.*
- **Health** *to boost our immune systems with pure food, clean water, and natural healing techniques.*

- **Wealth** *to feel the inner richness that we are all afforded in this life and to master the ability to create security for ourselves.*

Values make the world go 'round. They anchor in what matters most and serve as guiding principles for how we show up in life and how we do everything we do. The top values for Spiritual Sugar are Faith, Curiosity, Self-Care, Health and Wealth.

Here are some more **Spiritual Sugar Heart Sparks** to ignite your truth. Set a timer for a minimum of five minutes and dive in.

- Take a moment to journal about your VALUES.
- What are your top 5 values?
  What is your #1 value?
- When is the last time you did a values exercise to identify, review or refine your core values?
- How are you infusing values into everything you do?

_____

_____

_____

_____

_____

_____

_____

CHAPTER FIVE

Doing the Work

Where are YOU on your journey?

One of the most important parts of truly tapping into personal awareness is looking inward, giving yourself permission to examine what matters most, and being open to tuning in to your intuition.

On my healing with L♥VE journey, the two things that guided me to reclaim my Self, Health and Wealth were:

1) Faith
2) Intuition

I believe they go hand in hand and the closer you are to Source, the closer you are to intuitively knowing what is best for yourself. Because, when you tap into the pure energy of faith, intuition and your higher self, you can get clear guidance about what is best for you. Your clarity and connection to a Higher Power will allow you to move through situations, information, and differing views to tap into your core, divine truth and know what's best for you.

As I share specific tips to embrace healthier living, my goal is to inspire action that brings you closer to self, improves your health, and helps you redefine wealth. A big part of this will be asking YOU questions that you can apply to your life.

Let's start with making a date with YOU. One key component to healthier living and feeling inner peace is making time for YOU and giving yourself the space to examine and explore how you're showing up in life.

So, today, I suggest that you take yourself on a date. Go to a local bookstore, office supply outlet, gift card retailer, or the Dollar Store and get a journal. This journal will be your sacred space to set your own goals, write about how you'd like to improve your relationship with Self, Health and Wealth, and help set transformation in motion.

I highly recommend capturing your divine downloads in a journal because those ideas may point you in new directions and give you deeper insight into your life.

Keeping a journal has always been a big part of my life and it was paramount in my healing journey. In fact, I was first divinely guided to create Spiritual Sugar in August, 2015. At the time, I had no idea what it meant and I felt unequipped to address such a big topic. I was guided to write about it in my journal.

It was two years later in August, 2017 that I remembered the divine nudge and revisited my journal. In 2015, I knew I needed to make changes, I was digging deeper into my spirituality, and I was really stuck. When I look back, it seems that my intuition (and connection with Source) was trying to help me course-correct or at the very least give me heads up about what was to come. Interestingly enough, it was in August, 2017 that I was reminded of the journal entry and that I had two major surgeries to remove cancer. Revisiting this journal entry and the message about healing with L♥VE was a catalyst.

Go get your journal, take some time for YOU, and write about what you most want to experience in this world.

Here's your next **Spiritual Sugar Heart Spark**. Pause for a moment, pour yourself a cup of tea, set your timer for a minimum of five minutes and let your throughs flow.

How are your faith and intuition guiding you?

_____

_____

_____

_____

Facing Mortality is Not for The Faint of Heart

It's interesting to me how facing mortality impacts all areas of life.

One of the most important messages I received throughout my healing journey, besides "you will heal this with L♥VE" was *"Your number one priority is taking care of you."*

Instinctively I knew that is/was important and at the same time, I clearly hadn't been focused on myself as much as I could have been — otherwise, I wouldn't have gotten sick...

I now realize that this journey has taken a bigger toll on me than I had fully comprehended. While I kept it all together as best I could, took control of my health to save my life, managed to run my business (even though I did have to scale back considerably), a part of me was on autopilot.

One of the most mind-blowing revelations is that I have been filled with grief, guilt and shame about ever getting sick. Somehow these feelings subconsciously slipped in and have been gnawing on my soul. Even worse, these subconscious thoughts and feelings had been silently impacting my self-worth (no thanks to societal programming and misguided beliefs that it matters what other people think).

It feels like I'll be unpacking this for a while (and I actually think this is a good thing — realization leads to change). I share this with you today as an illustration of the importance of self-care.

No matter how well we feel, we're navigating something where there is usually a deeper layer to look at. This is exactly why it's important to nourish your body, mind and soul with positive experiences that allow you to go inward.

Spiritual Sugar is All about Healing with L♥VE

"Love is the energy that silently transfigures every situation.
~ David R. Hawkins

<u>Spiritual Sugar</u> by definition is: The inner sweetness of the soul.

It all begins within. This book is designed to help you tap into the inner sweetness of your soul and ignite self-love.

People have asked me about the title, sugar, and the relationship between sugar and cancer. While it's true that sugar can feed cancer, *Spiritual Sugar* can feed your soul (the title is also a divine download from Source, so who am I to argue).

In its pure form, sugar is natural. In small quantities, even good for you. But when people began processing it, roughly 2,500 years ago, it became an extremely unhealthy substance that's still in high demand despite the fact that it can cause extreme health problems. Hence, Spiritual Sugar is meant to bring you back to basics, to the natural form of who YOU truly are. And Sugar, coupled with Spiritual can align you with your higher self and help you tap into healing with L♥VE. Faith, intuition and Spiritual Sugar are some of the divine ingredients you can select to help heal yourself with L♥VE.

Let's take quick look at the definition of some key words per Merriam-Webster for context.

Spiritual by definition is as follows.

Adjective: of, relating to, consisting of, or affecting the spirit. of or relating to sacred matters. Of or relating to supernatural beings or phenomena. Concerned with religious values.

It's important to remember, though, that not all things that are spiritual or religious are holy. There's a popular meme that circulated on social media that says:

He: *"I'm Spiritual."*

She: *"Be more specific, demons are spiritual."*

I share this because salt and sugar look the same but they taste very different. The same can be said of a person's spiritual affiliation. That's why Spiritual Sovereignty and energetic integrity are paramount in your healing with L♥VE journey. Discernment is KEY.

Sugar by definition is:

a sweet crystallizable material that consists wholly or essentially of sucrose, is colorless or white when pure tending to brown when less refined, is obtained commercially from sugarcane or sugar beet and less extensively from sorghum, maples, and palms, and is important as a source of dietary carbohydrate and as a sweetener and preservative of other foods.

Interestingly enough, as a verb, the definition of sugar is: to make palatable or attractive (sweeten).

L♥VE by definition is:

strong affection for another arising out of kinship or personal ties. attraction based on sexual desire: affection and tenderness felt by lovers. Affection based on admiration, benevolence, or common interests. Warm attachment, enthusiasm, or devotion.

For the purposes of this book, we're focusing on <u>self-love</u> defined as:

> an appreciation of one's own worth or virtue. Proper regard for and attention to one's own happiness or well-being. inflated love of or pride in oneself.

In the context of healing with L♥VE, it's important to know that love is said to be the highest vibration and energy that moves through your heart, your mind, and your soul. There is also a frequency of vibration which connects the heart to the nature of love. When this energy vibrates at this frequency, whether in the form of light or sound, it will evoke feelings of love and connection. This frequency, known as the "miracle" note, is the frequency of 528Hz. Sound healing is a modality that can help heal on many levels.

Dr. Masaru Emoto[21] did many studies about the impacts of emotions, frequencies and intentions in relationship to water. Fear and negativity were shown to drastically reduce the quality of the water. Similar experiments have been done with food. In the book *E-Squared*, Pam Grout[27] offers nine experiments that prove your thoughts create your reality. When in doubt, check it out.

Energy and vibration matter. They are proven to impact everything. The energy you allow into your life impacts your frequency and vibration and it's important to be aware of this. If emotions and thoughts can impact the structure of water and food, imagine what they do to you on a cellular level in your body?

Another resource worth looking into is the book, **UNSTUCK:** *The Physics of Getting Out of Your Own Way* by Jennifer Hough.[26] Jennifer blends science, physics and spirituality in practical ways that demonstrate there are tangible, proven ways to manage your energy and create your reality.

CHAPTER SIX

My Personal Journal Entries

Duaring the entire healing with L♥VE journey, I kept notes in my private journal and shared notes in a secure, private PostHope[32] page for my sacred sphere of influence. This was my first post there to let everyone know how things were progressing. I kept this private because I refused and refuse to let cancer define me. I never referred to it as "mine" and treated it as a separate entity that simply had to go.

I even sent the cancer love, thanked it for the lesson and blessed it to leave my body so that I could do the work I'm intended to do on this earthly plane.

"The Scoop" is a chronicle of what led to me knowing something was seriously wrong (I've shared some of this before and this is a good recap of the start of the journey).

The Scoop — May 29, 2017

So... some of you know this and some of you don't. I'm not broadcasting this on social media and I'm keeping the circle tight. This seemed like the best way to connect the dots for my amazing support system that is sprinkled across the globe (you can sign up to get notifications of updates if you choose to stay in the loop).

There is never a good way to share news like this... But I know I am OK (as okay as living in the unknown can be). I have faith that I will heal this with ♥LOVE♥ and I will know more after my PET scan. For now, all I know is I had a tumor removed from my throat, the biopsy confirmed that it's T2 cancer of the tongue... squamous cell carcinoma (T2 means stage 2). It's rare in women — usually men who chew tobacco get it (but that's another story).

Here's what I want YOU to know. Cancer isn't necessarily a death sentence. I am not completely freaking out. In fact, I have a strange sense of calm that everything will be fine (with some fine-tuning). In addition to mainstream options (which I may or may not choose), there are many holistic approaches to healing cancer (I'll share some resources later). This means we can have normal conversations about normal things and that I'm not completely falling apart, although I do have my moments.

I am holding absolute faith that the biopsy removed it all and that is that. We will know for sure after the PET scan (which doesn't seem to be a priority for the medical community at this point). Right now, the hardest part is not knowing. The PET scan will give us the information we need to know what we're dealing with (basically they will fill me with some radioactive gunk and do a full body x-ray/scan to see if and where the cancer has spread).

For now, I'm focused on extreme self-care. This includes rest, natural supplements (herbs/essential oils), a super clean diet, meditation, massages, sound therapy, walking and more. My diet was already rather healthy but now I must stay away from all processed foods and processed sugar — sugar feeds cancer — limit cheese, chocolate, wine, coffee and alcohol — BOO!

So, how did we get here? (Full details because I get tired talking about it — and a little pissed too.)

For at least 6 months (probably more like a year), I've had extreme fatigue, headaches (migraine — which is new), shortness of breath, chest pain, and pain in my left ear. In the past year, I've had a couple of sinus colds that really took me out (unusual for me). My primary care provider knew about all of this, told me to walk and take multi-vitamins. As I look back, I've been having the shortness of breath for a long time... since at least last October.

In March, I started feeling something in my throat. It was the week before I was filming a new copywriting training course for my biz (the week of the 13th). I thought maybe I was just trying to get out of being on video by getting sick (not a super fan of being on camera). So, I pushed through but the irritation in my throat got worse and it felt like something was growing in there. The best way to describe it is that I felt like I imagine a cat feels when they have a hairball. It was getting difficult to swallow and food was getting caught in my throat.

On Thursday, March 30th, I went to see my regular NP (nurse practitioner). She suspected there may be some kind of infection, couldn't see anything in my throat, suggested I make an appointment with the dentist, and prescribed Amoxicillin. I went to Los Angeles that next week for a week and got really sick while there (was in bed for a full day with multiple symptoms including what I suspected could be acid reflux — I'll spare you the details).

I scheduled another appointment as soon as I got back to Oregon and was able to get in on April 11th. This was the appointment that solidified the need to get a new primary physician.

In a nutshell, I had already submitted all my symptoms and concerns into the computerized system when I made my appointment. When I got there, they thought I was there for acid reflux (note, that was a self-diagnosis on my part and really a guess — as well as just one of multiple symptoms). I — AGAIN — shared all my symptoms and she asked me what I thought it was. I, having no idea, said, "I don't know." She asked me a few more times and my answer was the same (a little thing about never going to medical school precluded me from knowing what was going on but I knew something was really wrong).

Then she asked, "Do you think you have cancer?"

I was stunned. I hadn't given that any energy. She continued to tell me, "Your cholesterol is horrible."

Something I already knew and one of the reasons I'd already changed my diet and am walking more (which I shared with her while in disbelief at how she was speaking to me). Then she said, "I don't' know where to start. You have so much going on and I cannot just put all of you in an x-ray machine."

After soaking in this major WTF moment, I said, "Maybe we should start with my throat since there is something growing in there?" That's how I got a referral to an ENT (Ear, Nose and Throat) specialist and she ordered another round of blood tests.

I had to push to get an earlier appointment with the ENT (it was originally scheduled for some time in May). The growth in my throat was getting bigger and I had 18 days to ponder the "C" word while I waited to get in (it's interesting what the thought of having cancer can do to your mind let alone actually having it — kind of stressful).

My appointment with the Ear, Nose and Throat Specialist (who is awesome) on April 28 determined that I had a growth in my throat that was now almost 2 centimeters big (about an inch). We scheduled a biopsy for May 5 (not usually how I celebrate Cinco de Mayo). Mom came and went with me (I have the most awesome parents on the planet). The follow-up appointment to discuss biopsy results was scheduled for May 16.

I established a new primary care practitioner (Internal Medicine). My first appointment with her was on May 11. This is the same day I had a dentist appointment (routine cleaning scheduled because my previous health-care practitioner thought I had an abscessed tooth, and in fact, that's what she diagnosed my condition to be — FIRED!). Anyway, my new physician is wonderful, she scheduled new cholesterol panels because they had not been checked for two years and also scheduled a stress test to determine why I have shortness of breath and chest pain (this test happened on May 31 — results are pending).

On May 16, Mom and I went to my follow-up with my ENT Specialist and he shared the biopsy results confirming that I have cancer. We discovered that he removed a walnut-sized tumor during the biopsy (surgery through my mouth and down my throat — no idea how he did that as I was clearly out). We are still in hurry up and wait mode as the PET Scan needs to be scheduled. I called Oregon Imaging to check on status on Monday, May 23. They informed me they have the paperwork but have to put it in their computer systems before they can schedule an appointment and that could take at least two days. They also indicated that the earliest appointment for the PET scan is on the May 30 but that it will likely be full by the time they get my paperwork in the computer (seriously!?). So, we're in hurry up and wait mode. I called my ENT Specialist's office and left a message to see if they can expedite and I'll check with my new physician too. I thought it would be a good idea to keep a running log of all of this because it's become clear that we must manage our own health and PUSH for what we need.

As I'm writing this, I just got notification that my PET Scan is on June 6.

In general, I know there are several possibilities:

1) My ENT Specialist got all the cancer when he biopsied a walnut-sized tumor
2) The PET Scan reveals that it's gone or that it has been found in other areas
3) We determine a healing plan of action once we know. That could include surgery, laser treatment, radiation, or chemo (or a combo)

The good news is I have insurance that covers most of this but not holistic options and natural supplements, etc. I am most interested in alternative approaches as chemo and radiation are so toxic.

Currently my biggest challenge is that I need to conserve my energy and continue to run my business. While doing so, I'll need to scale back quite a bit to focus on healing although I am determined to continue working while healing (I L♥VE what I do). Thankfully, family is helping out where they can. I did not have the foresight to invest in disability insurance and am pretty certain I cannot get it now and I cannot afford NOT to work. I am a pre-existing condition.

You, as a part of my sacred sphere of influence, can help by remaining positive, sending prayers, meditation or whatever your thing might be — I welcome all good, healing energy. I've been doing tons of research and some info you might find helpful are listed below.

Book: *Radical Remission* by Kelly Turner[2] (the audio is great and I also have the physical book version) — this focuses on the 9 key areas that Cancer Thrivers (I like that better than survivors) have in common. The only two that are "tangible" are exercise and diet. All others are spiritual, faith-based, alternative healing, and positive attitude-oriented (all of which make a huge difference in healing). Get your copy here http://amzn.to/2BCOuT5

Docu-Series: *The Truth About Cancer*[1] — you can catch the first two segments here http://bit.ly/CancerTHETruth — If you don't want to join their mailing list, just watch episode 1 and 2 below — this will seriously blow your mind. (Do yourself a favor and watch them — knowledge in power and action gets results). It did mine and it gave me hope and a sincere belief that it's totally possible to heal cancer with L♥VE (and the right foods, etc.)... I highly recommend diving into the entire series.

The Truth About Cancer[1] Episode 1: https://go2.thet-ruthaboutcancer.com/agq-encore/episode-1/
The Truth About Cancer[1] Episode 2: https://go2.thet-ruthaboutcancer.com/agq-encore/episode-2/

I have eliminated alcohol, sugar, cheese and coffee from my diet and incorporated more fresh fruit and veggies. I'm also drinking only filtered water (the chemicals in our water are another major health risk factor). One of the key components to healing is your diet and most of the food we are eating, especially processed food, is killing us. Another key component of healing is exercise and I'm walking more too. An interesting FACTOID from the *Radical Remission* book — of the 9 Factors that people who have successfully healed cancer have in common, 7 are mostly spiritual, positive attitude, faith-based, and energy healing work.

I ask that you keep a positive attitude. I'm OK with people knowing but I'd prefer to keep it private so, please, only share the link to this page privately with people we are connected to and I don't want this mentioned on social media (I trust your discretion AND if you mention it to someone we're closely connected to and they don't know yet, let them know it's because I'm pretty busy trying to keep my life in order — nothing personal). I only want people who have faith in miracles and full-on belief that we can heal cancer with L♥VE chiming in (that's YOU, my sacred sphere of influence). If you have information on natural, alternative treatments that have been effective for others, please feel free to share (you can add this info as a comment — see bottom of page — so I have it all in one place).

Many have asked how you can support. For now, send love, prayers, good juju, and healing vibes. I'm not fighting this thing — I'm healing it with L♥VE and I'm certainly not ready to check out. I 100% believe that pushing against anything amplifies it so let's focus on a happy, healthy outcome. I'm not good at asking for help but I might need it depending on the outcome and I'll keep everyone posted. ♥BIG LOVE♥

Unraveling in LA

April 2017: I flew to the Los Angeles area to spend time with family, hang out with a gal pal, and attend a business event. I knew intuitively something BIG was off. I also knew that no matter what it was I wanted to have this experience (even if it was one of the last experiences I ever had). My spidey sense was kicking in and intuition was on high alert. At the same time, I was still trusting my health-care practitioner even though I also knew, deep down inside, that what I was feeling was not an abscessed tooth.

I pressed on and ended up flat on my back. Luckily I was at my aunt's house because I literally could not get out of bed. I'll spare you the details of all of the symptoms but know this... my body was not digging the antibiotics and everything else that was going on. I managed to pull it together to attend the business event but I kept to myself and retreated to my room after session. To wrap up the trip, I spent time with a dear friend and we went for our favorite hike around Terranea Resort. She noticed my breathing... it was labored and even a mini hike was wiping me out. We've been friends for over 30 years and she knew something was wrong. I knew something was wrong. If only my health-care practitioner would listen and take my concerns seriously. I had more symptoms to add to the long list that I'd already been sharing. AND I intended to get answers.

I feel something growing in my throat and it is getting bigger every day.

The Ultrasound

4/20/17: One of the tests that was ordered while I waited to get into the ENT was an Ultrasound.

My symptoms were varied and included:

- Headaches *(a migraine at one point — so severe I couldn't do anything)*
- Deep chest pain *(they did an EKG and it was clear)*
- Shortness of breath
- Shoulder pain *(in my left shoulder)*
- Night sweats
- Earaches
- Chronic fatigue
- Vertigo
- Discomfort in my throat *(because I felt something growing in there)*

I had already lost a lot of faith in my health-care practitioner (NP). I was trying NOT to judge. I know we are all just people and then... THIS happened.

I received the results from the throat ultrasound via email. NO call from my NP (nurse practitioner — the one I eventually fired). According to the report, I have a cyst in my throat. I assume it's infected as it has a serpentine quality and it feels like it's moving — much like the moving back pain I experienced when I had a major kidney infection (that's the only thing I have to compare it to). I assume the cyst is starting to drain but these assumptions are my own. I have not heard from the NP. It feels weird now — smaller — but as if it's spread in a spiderweb-like fashion. I actually feel it moving and spreading. I went for a full-body massage and mini-facial and have been taking oregano oil internally to help amplify my wellness naturally. I've also been using Deep Blue on my shoulder. Plus, On Guard and Breathe topically (on my chest and bottoms of my feet). I'm drinking lots of tea with honey, spearmint, lavender and lemon essential oils. I've added other natural healing aids for good measure. I pray this is something minor. I cannot get into the ENT till the 3rd...

*Note: What I was experiencing was NOT a cyst. It was the cancer moving and growing and I could feel it. So weird.

A Miracle and Next Steps

6/11/17: The meeting with the Oncologist/Radiologist confirmed that my PET/CT scan were free and clear and classified as "normal." This is something the doctor has not seen often. I know it's a miracle. The next step is to meet with my ENT (Ear, Nose and Throat Specialist) and determine a follow-up plan.

It was mentioned that radiation is an option (although at this point, I'm not going to do that) and suggested that I confer with the ENT to see if he feels surgery is in order to ensure zero margins (margins are the outer perimeter of where the tumor was.)

Coloring Outside the Lines
AND Paying Attention to Margins...

Throughout the healing with L♥VE journey, I had to face big realities, facing mortality was perhaps one of the biggest. Healing with L♥VE was my overall approach, it took many tools to heal. Including surgery...

6/14/17: I'm feeling a little nervous and grateful all at the same time. I spoke with my ENT Specialist and he recommends a transoral robotic surgery and a neck dissection surgery to ensure zero margins. He suspects that if we don't do this, the cancer has a greater likelihood of coming back. Although he did remove the tumor during the biopsy, it was not a full surgery.

Additionally, he's recommending that I have the procedure done at OHSU[22] (Oregon Health and Science University). This is a state-of-the-art medical school in Portland that is doing the most advanced robotic surgeries around. They have the capability to do the surgery orally with the use of a robotic arm. This is a better option than traditional surgery because it will not require making external incisions from the outside that could also include breaking my jaw to get to where they need to go. One of my ENT Specialist's partners has done robotic resections but not as frequently as the OHSU[22] team. So, that's why they are referring me on...

Now, it's more "hurry up and wait" while my ENT Specialist's team coordinates with OHSU[22] to see when I can have a consultation and determine the next steps. All in all, this sounds WAY better than radiation, which is not at all appealing. They will be doing surgery on my tongue and this method has a positive recovery rate that doesn't require rebuilding tissue (basically my tongue will heal on its own). My ENT Specialist says that I'm the ideal poster child for these procedures and this can mean that I won't require any radiation or chemo.

All I know for now is that I'll likely be going to Portland. It will likely be an inpatient procedure and I'll probably have to NOT work for a bit. I am not exactly sure how I'll manage all of this but I have faith that it will all work out somehow.

I'm calling on you for more love, prayers, good juju, white light and positive thoughts. This experience is not for the faint of heart.

I am thankful and know I still must be diligent.

The Final Phase... (pre-surgery)

July of 2017 was an emotionally intense time... when you face mortality, you don't take anything lightly — at least I didn't. My family and I traveled to Portland to have meetings with the OHSU[22] team in preparation for my surgeries in August of 2017. This is an entry from my PostHope[32] journal about the process. I had to do a lot of mental preparation, tap into my faith and accept whatever might come my way...

7/24/17: As my dance with cancer continues, I continue to be grateful for the love and support of my family and friends. That's YOU! And a special thanks to those who have signed up to get notifications when I update this site. It's so much easier for me to share everything here instead of repeating myself.

Mom, Dad and I went to Portland to meet with my Head and Neck Surgeon at OHSU[22] last week. I'm still energetically recovering from the trip as the drive and the reality of the next steps have wiped me out to the core.

The good news is we're nearing the final phase of completely removing all remnants of cancer. The reality is, my Head and Neck Surgeon is recommending surgery to remove the margins in my throat (margins are the surrounding area where the tumor was — they take the edges out to ensure no fragments of cancer are left) via Transoral robotic surgery and a neck dissection to remove potentially impacted lymph nodes.

Although the PET/CT scans were clear, my ENT Specialist, Radiologist Oncologist and Head and Neck Surgeon all believe there are likely small traces of cancer left near where the tumor was and there is a 40% chance the lymph nodes have been impacted. I'm told, if I choose not to have the neck dissection, it could cause future complications should the cancer come back. So, in this case, it's best to be proactive.

I feel confident with the OHSU[22] team and I'm thankful for the expert medical care in Oregon. These are not minor procedures and will require a hospital stay at OHSU[22] for 3 to 5 days and I'll likely have to be on a feeding tube for a few days (looking into healthy nutrients as an alternative to the Jevity that the hospital uses as standard feeding tube fuel — it's full of high fructose corn syrup and other things I'd prefer not to put in my body).

I've also been advised that I will need A LOT of rest before the procedure and after. My Head and Neck Surgeon recommends NOT working for two to three weeks (he's mostly referencing talking on the phone and seeing clients in person — I will likely be able to do light computer work). Thankfully, my clients are awesome and those I'm working with closely right now are aware of the situation. At the same time, I am going to call on the support of friends and family more than ever during this time.

The surgery will take place in August — possibly the 10th, 11th or 18th but maybe even earlier than that. I hear back from scheduling tomorrow. For now, I'm trying to remain centered, focused on positive healing outcomes, and preparing for the final phase. As always, prayers, healing thoughts and good juju are appreciated. ♥

On The Road to Recovery

Throughout this journey, I was, and am determined to heal with L♥VE. When they told me I'd have to leave the hospital with a feeding tube, I proved them wrong. I weaned myself off the pain pills as soon as possible AND I planned adventures that guaranteed I'd have to recover quickly. Here's a journal entry from my private PostHope[32] page to give you a little more insight into the healing journey.

10/10/2017: Today marks two months since my surgery date. On September 20, I flew to Portland and back for my first follow-up after my surgeries with my Head and Neck Surgeon. THAT was a long day but all went well. He assured me that things are healing as they should. I might be a tad impatient (totally grateful but ready to be healed).

My Head and Neck Surgeon says it will take a couple more months for things to fully heal. That includes the incision on my neck and the internal healing where the tumor once was. I am experiencing pain in my left shoulder, chest, arm, and neck and this is part of the side effects from having the neck dissection. When they took my lymph nodes (16 of them I believe), they had to cut through nerves. During the healing process, I feel the nerves trying to refire/reconnect but it's kind of a weird feeling. I have full intentions of getting complete feeling back (right now part of my ear, cheek, neck, and chest are numb). The good news is, everything is clear and I'm set to see my ENT Specialist every 6 to 8 weeks for follow-up in Medford and will see my Head and Neck Surgeon in Portland once a quarter or so.

When I got back from Portland, I packed for a weekend retreat in Mount Shasta and I also went to my favorite mineral springs nearby. From there, I took the back roads (and I do mean back roads) to meander from Mt. Shasta to Humboldt. I took Rural Route Forest Road 17 over to the Lake Trinity Area and finally to Humboldt to see my Mom and Dad. I was gone for about two weeks and it was a much-needed journey. On the way, I picked up a beautiful Rose Quartz Heart to help accelerate the healing.

I'm back in Ashland now. The leaves are turning and it's beautiful. My next steps are meeting with homeopathic, naturopathic and functional doctors who are able to connect the dots between nutrition and health. Sadly, Western Medicine is lacking in that department and most doctors only get one to two weeks of basic nutrition. For example, I no longer eat processed sugar since it feeds cancer and I plan to stay healthy for a long time. I've also eliminated all processed foods, alcohol and coffee. When I was in the hospital and on a feeding tube for multiple days, they fed me the standard "Ensure-like" feeding tube gunk that has high fructose corn syrup, very little nutritional value and only maintains calorie levels (that's what they are concerned about). They were not sure why my glycemic index kept skyrocketing. I'm not a doctor, and I could tell them exactly why. There's a natural, healthy option but it wasn't considered because they said insurance won't cover it (even though I indicated I'd be happy to pay the difference).

My point is this: WE must be our own advocates. PERIOD. And what we eat and drink does impact our health despite what doctors might say (and mine have admittedly stated that they don't know much about that). Please note: I am not bashing them — they do an excellent job and they stay in their lane. Now it's time for me to connect the dots. I also start working with a Myofascial release specialist next week to massage my neck and shoulder area to help regain full feeling and movement.

I've had to make a lot of changes and I'm learning to live life in a different way. I feel better, still tired, but I'm blessed and I know that's true. I'm working part-time on client projects and trying not to push myself too hard but the reality is... life must go on.

Thanks again for your love and support. I appreciate each of you so much. ♥

Another God Nudge

In early 2020 before the pandemic was in full swing, I attended an intimate talk hosted by Neale Donald Walsch[13] about *Conversations With God* at a local tea house in Ashland, Oregon. As he often does, he opened the floor to questions after the discussion.

I felt drawn to ask Neale a question in relationship to my healing with love journey and the divine charge to write a book about it.

I shared that I'm a cancer thriver and that I received a God Nudge to write a book about healing with L♥VE. I mentioned my story was already featured in the book *The Silver Lining of Cancer*.[3] I told him I found it interesting that I received this message two years prior to the cancer diagnosis and I didn't feel qualified to write the book and didn't fully understand WHY I was given this charge. I felt overwhelmed by the message, and journaled about it, while having a major "Who am I?" moment about the entire thing. I wondered if it was necessary to go through this journey and cancer diagnosis in order to do "the work" I'm being divinely guided to do. I was referencing the book, this book, that God told me to write.

Neale laughed, a knowing laugh, and his response was, "Absolutely NOT. Some people just need to get hit upside the head by the proverbial two by four. Who are you not to?! Don't you dare not write that book."

And the rest is history. *Spiritual Sugar* is all about healing with L♥VE, and I for one, know the world needs more healing and more love.

CHAPTER SEVEN

The Silver Lining of Cancer

In 2019, two years after the cancer diagnosis and successfully healing with L♥VE, I was invited by my dear friend Tracey Ehman to be a co-author of the #1 International Bestselling book *The Silver Lining of Cancer: 13 Courageous Women Share Their Inspirational Stories After a Life-Changing Diagnosis.*[3]

Tracey was adamant the world needed to learn about my Healing with L♥VE Journey. Here's what I shared in the chapter I wrote for that book. Some of what I share here has been touched on in my personal journal entries and it's an important message worth repeating.

> *"I will never attend an anti-war rally;*
> *if you have a peace rally, invite me."*
> ~ Mother Teresa

Healing with L♥VE

"Do you think you have cancer?"

This question stunned me. I was almost speechless that a health-care practitioner would ask me this. There's a little thing like never going to medical school that precluded me from having the answer to this question. After all, I was there to get a professional opinion.

I knew something big was going on, but I didn't know what. My health-care practitioner at the time insisted that what I was experiencing was an abscessed tooth. I *knew* that wasn't what it was, but I never in a million years imagined it was cancer. My airway was tightening, I was having trouble breathing and swallowing, and I could *feel* something growing in my throat.

This was April 2017. It would be weeks until I could get into the ENT (Ear Nose Throat) specialist. Weeks of wondering, *What if I do have cancer?* Thankfully, the divinely guided message I received was "You're going to heal this with L♥VE." I held on to faith with the occasional thought of *Am I being delusional? What if I die tomorrow?*

The truth is I was OK with either outcome. When I assessed my life, my life was rich. A quick inventory revealed that the only things I still wanted to accomplish were 1) publish my book(s); 2) go to Italy; and 3) visit the rain forest.

Of course, I thought of my parents. I also thought of meeting my soul partner. But all in all, I was good with my life, and I still am. In fact, it's become even richer.

As I sat in inquiry, I said a prayer to thank God for my life, acknowledged that this was *way* bigger than me, and expressed my gratitude for everything I'd already experienced throughout this lifetime. I added "I'm OK with the outcome either way, but I'm really not ready to check out, and I think You have more work for me to do in this world." I settled into absolute faith that all would be exactly as it should be, and I followed divine guidance throughout the entire process.

In the United States, one in two women and one in three men will be diagnosed with some type of cancer in their lifetime. A recent study in the UK indicates that it's more like one in every two people. Cancer is not discriminating. There are more than one hundred types of cancer, and as you're reading this, that means either you or I have been diagnosed or will be diagnosed (statistically speaking). In this case, it was me. On May 16, 2017, I heard the words, "You have cancer."... or it might have been "It is cancer."... either way, these three words are not words I'd wish upon anyone. Nonetheless, I did not let this define me, nor did I accept it as "mine," and I was determined to heal with L♥VE.

Instead, I embraced self-care and that became my number-one priority. It should be yours too.

Healing with L♥VE Transforms Everything

Taking control of my health and choosing ME has been an amazing journey and a true testament of faith. I encourage *you* to choose YOU so you can take control of your health and hopefully avoid any serious health care wake-up calls.

I underwent two major surgeries on August 10, 2017. I kept it quiet. I relied upon my sacred sphere of influence to be my support system, and I focused on embracing wellness. What I know for sure is that I am delighted to be a thriver. I prefer the term *thriver* over *survivor* because that's what I am. I turned my health around to thrive without chemo or radiation.

The cancer is now gone, and I am on a continuous healing journey. I've released forty pounds, eliminated all processed food, changed my entire life for the better, and continue to focus on healing with L♥VE. I received the official five-year "all clear, you're cured" report in August of 2022.

I think Mother Teresa said it best when she said, "I will never attend an anti-war rally; if you have a peace rally, invite me." She had it dialed in. When we wage war on anything or rally against anything or declare a battle to fight against something, we create more momentum *for* the very thing we are against. Words have energy, and my focus is healing with L♥VE.

I understand this may seem counterintuitive to most (welcome to my world), but it is pure truth. It's what I've been teaching in the context of my work, it's what Mother Teresa so eloquently shared with a simple quote, and it's what the world needs to course-correct — *it is pure love.*

When we want to change something, we must engage in full-on LOVE, not wage war.

We must flip the script and focus only on the positive outcome.

We must take positive, proactive action instead of inciting riled-up reaction.

This is not a new concept. I cannot take full credit for it; I can only live it and invite you to do the same.

This doesn't mean we won't be challenged. This doesn't mean we won't get ticked off at circumstances. This doesn't mean that we won't feel despair based on world affairs.

We are human. We will *feel.* We will *live* and hopefully we will *love.*

I believe we can heal anything with love. And to do that we must start somewhere.

With ourselves. With our families. With our friends. With our communities. With our world.

- ♥ Love yourself — treat yourself well; be kind.

- ♥ Love your family — which often means forgiveness and understanding.

- ♥ Love your friends — reach out and let them know how much they mean to you.

- ♥ Love your community — get involved; small acts have big impact.

- ♥ Love your world — take care of this precious resource we have been given.

And, yes, I know, life will rock you to the core. It may make you want to wage war but remember: the only thing that ever really heals is love.

When we combine love with knowledge and action, we have the power to facilitate great change in the world.

My Top Lessons from Healing Cancer with L♥VE

1) Focus on *life*. When you push against anything, it creates more of what you don't want. It's important to focus on healing, not fighting, battling, or conquering. The language we use creates our reality.

2) You are 100 percent responsible for taking control of your health. Learn about nutrition, healthy eating, and how to fuel your body the right way.

3) Question everything. Get a second opinion (or more). Push for what you need. Don't take no for an answer.

4) Health-care practitioners don't know everything. I was initially misdiagnosed with an abscessed tooth. When in reality, I had a rapidly growing aggressive cancerous tumor in my throat. Had I listened and trusted this misdiagnosis, I wouldn't be writing this today. #truth

5) Doctors are valuable resources. They do stay in their lane, though. So, focus on what you know will improve your health beyond what the doctors tell you (research nutrition and real food). It took surgery *and* a complete dietary reset to heal with L♥VE.

6) People don't know how to deal with cancer. So, when people do show up, it means a lot. More than *you* will ever

know. When people don't show up, it hurts. More than you will ever know.

7) Cancer is becoming "normal." Let that sink in. There is nothing normal about this. That means it's up to you and me to boost our immune systems, eliminate toxins in our homes, reduce stress, eat more fruits and vegetables (preferably organic), eliminate processed poisonous foods, take the time to educate ourselves about what it takes to live a healthy life, and incorporate what we learn.

The truth is, we are not promised tomorrow.

When people showed up, it meant the world to me. For those who would have liked to show up but didn't know, I'm sorry. I had to keep this within the sacred sphere of influence, and when you're facing something like this, it's hard to reach out (especially when you do and . . . crickets).

Many have asked me to share what I did to turn my health around. It's important to know that every cancer is different, every person is different, and that means what I did worked for *me*. It's not a guarantee for anyone else. We all must take our health into our own hands and make ourselves — and of course, our families — the priority.

For now, I'm simply grateful. Grateful for every breath. Grateful for those who bring peace and positivity into my life. Grateful for my family, my friends, my health, my fabulous clients, and life.

I invite you to sprinkle a little "spiritual sugar" on your life by redefining your relationships with Self, Health, and Wealth. It all starts with you.

Every minute and every second is precious. Combine love with knowledge and action and we have the power to facilitate great change in the world.

Here's another **Spiritual Sugar Heart Spark**. Set your timer for a minimum of five minutes and dive in to explore this prompt.

Where are you starting with L♥VE today?

_____

_____

_____

_____

_____

_____

_____

_____

_____

CHAPTER EIGHT

My Question for YOU

On June 21, 2017, this divinely guided question was delivered to me. AND I am asking it of YOU before we dive into the rest of the content including the Spiritual Sugar principles. Your answer to this ***Spiritual Sugar Heart Spark*** could change everything for you.

What IF heaven IS earth?
How would YOU behave differently?

Take a moment to journal your thoughts about this... It might just change everything for YOU. Be sure to set your timer for at least 20 minutes now, so you don't move past this.

_____

_____

_____

_____

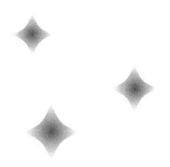

SECTION 2

Spiritual Tools

CHAPTER NINE

Will YOU Commit to YOU?

There is something life-affirming and soul-opening about facing mortality. It's the ultimate choice point to COMMIT to YOU. I'm reminded of this every anniversary of the two major surgeries to remove a rare and aggressive cancer from my body. And I CELEBRATE being cancer-free. I encourage you to pause and give thanks for your life today because we are not promised tomorrow.

My healing with L♥VE journey allowed me to look deeply at everything that matters in my life (and what really doesn't). I have always shared that this "life" is not a dress rehearsal. This is a core, universal truth. We may stumble, fall, course-correct, and learn from our mistakes but, THIS is IT.

I was asked in an interview about how I chose L♥VE over FEAR to heal.

My answer is simple yet complex.

1) **You must have faith** — a belief in something bigger than you. I'm not just talking spiritual or religious beliefs although these beliefs can be a great starting point. I'm talking about a deep knowing that there is a greater life

force outside of you that is guided by pure light. When you tap into your heart, your intuition and the magic of life, you'll begin to notice miracles all around you. Pause for a moment and look at nature. If you're ever questioning if there is something greater than you at play in the world, pause and look at nature. Or, better yet, take a hike, visit a local park and tap into the beauty that surrounds you. Faith and nature played a big part in my healing journey and they can make a difference for you, too.

2) **You must develop a practice** (or multiple practices) that connect you with this source regularly so that your faith is amplified. This could be walking in nature, prayers, meditation, journaling, or whatever makes your soul sing and tap into the miracle of life.

3) **You must commit to YOU**. This means fueling your body, mind, and spirit with the purest of thoughts, foods, and nutrients (hint: if you cannot pronounce it, don't eat it).

4) AND finally, **practicing gratitude is KEY**. If you are not thankful for every second, minute, breath, and experience that you are creating in your life (the good and the bad), it's time to course-correct. Life is a gift, breathing is a gift, and taking time to embody the richness of life and be present in the moment is vital to creating more joy and life force.

It's also important to gain some deep inner clarity and connection to your Higher Power so you're guided to surround yourself with people, places, and things that nourish and uplift your soul. And, I must add a word of caution: Committing to YOU will rock you to the core. Your elevated vibration will vibrate people who are not aligned right out of your life. This is a good thing and it can be painful. The brighter your light shines, the louder the naysayers get and the more important it is to have a trusted sacred sphere of influence. When you are fully tapped into Source, you can create a new paradigm where your vibration attracts elevated people, places and experiences. When you feel something is off or you're experiencing less than optimal encounters on any level, that's a telltale sign that it's time to course-correct and align with the Divine. The more you embrace divinity, the more potent your energy will be.

Committing to YOU is deep work; you have to look at your shadows and release what no longer serves you. This means releasing the old stories that keep you stuck (and are often a false and broken self-protection mechanism), acknowledging and letting go of unhealthy patterns, and opening your heart to creating a life that supports you on all levels. I promise it will be worth it. YOU are worth it.

So, as I celebrate being cancer-free, I ask you this: What will you do to COMMIT to YOU today?

_____

_____

_____

_____

Your NEXT Steps

Now it's time to dig a little deeper. To unearth the unspoken, the parts of you that are seemingly broken. In order to fully embody the concept of healing with L♥VE, you have to give yourself some love. This means releasing what no longer serves, and examining the things that leave us feeling defeated, unworthy, unhealthy or without passion for life. Because, if you leave these things alone, buried in your subconscious, unconscious or masked by addictions and distractions, they will manifest themselves in the form of illness in your body. Hence the cancer diagnosis that I received...

So, what does this mean? It means that anything that's ever happened to you in this lifetime and other lifetimes greatly impacts you on a cellular and spiritual level and can affect your health. This doesn't actually mean you're broken, but it does mean you can course-correct and repair any damage that has been done.

Here's a list of experiences that can fracture our body, soul, and psyche (things we must learn to release and leave behind).

- Trauma caused before birth in the womb
- Ancestral trauma
- Past life trauma
- Physical abuse
- Mental abuse
- Psychological abuse
- Sexual abuse
- Verbal abuse
- Financial abuse
- Domestic abuse of any kind
- Addictions
- Eating disorders
- Mental disorders
- Depression
- Anxiety
- Natural disasters
- Severe illness or injury
- The death of a loved one
- Witnessing an act of violence
- Self-deprecating humor and behavior
- Unhealthy patterns of any kind
- Feelings of failure
- Feelings of self-loathing
- Feelings of not enough
- Worthiness issues
- Inability to forgive yourself for mistakes

- Not speaking your truth or owning your voice (suppressing feelings)
- Being belittled or not supported in your creative expression

_____

_____

_____

_____

_____

Fill in the blanks with anything I haven't mentioned that you may have consciously or subconsciously/unconsciously experienced that doesn't serve you. I highly recommend that you set a timer for five minutes and give this some attention in the moment. We are all a little cracked and we can fill the cracks with gold. The Japanese word kintsugi means "joining with gold." This centuries-old art is more than an aesthetic, it's part of a broader philosophy of embracing the beauty of human flaws.

So, as you look at healing yourself with L♥VE and think of the Japanese art of putting broken pottery pieces back together with gold, you can consider this a metaphor for embracing your flaws and imperfections. And realize there is perfection in our imperfections and we all have the power to heal.

That being said, it's good to remember that we cannot give from an empty cup, even when we've filled the cracks with gold. Here's why addressing and releasing what no longer serves is so important. For the sake of keeping things streamlined and simple, I'm going to touch on:

- Abuse
- Trauma
- Addictions

I have found that these are the three areas that can take you out if you're not careful. When you're repressing, experiencing or have experienced abuse, trauma or addiction, the byproduct is often low self-esteem, depression, anxiety, fear and even PTSD (post-traumatic stress disorder). It's important that you understand I'm not a doctor or a psychologist. I'm simply a soul having a human experience and these are some of the things I've noticed either personally, via friends and family, or through research.

ABUSE

According to the Social Care Institute for Excellence[35], there are ten main types of abuse.

- Physical abuse
- Domestic violence or abuse
- Sexual abuse
- Psychological or emotional abuse
- Financial or material abuse
- Modern slavery
- Discriminatory abuse
- Organizational or institutional abuse
- Neglect or acts of omission
- Self-neglect

Experiencing any type of abuse will often lead to a trauma response. This can show up in a myriad of ways and it can also be repressed, not shared, and held in — which in turn can cause health issues to manifest.

How has abuse shown up in your life? When you identify it, you can heal it (it may take the help of a trusted therapist). Set your timer for at least five minutes and give yourself permission to explore how abuse has or may be impacting you.

_____

_____

_____

_____

_____

TRAUMA

When you have been abused in any way, and we all have been abused in some way in this lifetime, there may or may not be telltale signs. One coping mechanism is to "stuff" or repress the memories to create the illusion of safety by not addressing what has happened, not getting professional support, and/or not doing the deep shadow work needed to release yourself from trauma. While repression is a common coping mechanism, it will not help you heal and until you have addressed and released the stress held in your body from ANY trauma you have experienced, you are likely making yourself sick. Stress is the #1 cause of many ailments in society today and stress definitely impacts the immune system and creates an environment for ailments to take hold, including cancer.

According to Psych Guides,[33] trauma can surface days, weeks, months or years after an event actually happens. Often when you've experienced trauma, you might be edgy, jumpy, seem shaken or disoriented or develop high levels of anxiety. Anxiety can cause a variety of symptoms like night terrors, edginess, irritability, poor concentration, changes in personality, panic attacks, and mood swings (while these are common signs of anxiety, trauma can show up in many other ways). Sometimes trauma can go completely unnoticed because self-protection mechanisms kick in to hide the truth. Often, friends and family will have no idea you've been traumatized and when the trauma is deeply repressed, you may not even remember it on the surface either. That's why it's always important to go deep and look for the root cause of EVERYTHING. There is usually a good reason for the way people behave and sometimes we're simply responding with fight, flight or freeze instincts that appear to keep us safe.

Here's more food for thought. Set your timer and go deep.

How is trauma shaping your life and the way you respond to life?

_____

_____

_____

_____

_____

ADDICTIONS

Addiction comes in all forms and is often triggered by abuse and trauma. When our minds have trouble processing challenging things that we've experienced, we crave an escape. That escape can come in many forms and these addictions are hard to shake until you go deep and look at the root cause. These addictive behaviors are a symptom of something more and unfortunately, too few people choose to do the work.

- Alcohol addiction
- Prescription drug addiction
- Drug addiction
- Heroin addiction
- Opioid addiction
- Nicotine addiction
- Sexual addiction
- Gambling

When you find yourself leaning on any of these crutches, it's a good idea to get some outside support in the form of professional counseling or therapy.

From a spiritual perspective, addictions can open you up to unsavory energy and entities.

For example, let's look at alcohol addiction. The word "Alcohol" comes from Arabic "al-kuhl," which means "BODY EATING SPIRIT" and gives root origins to the English term of "Ghoul."

"In alchemy, alcohol is used to extract the soul essence of an 'entity,'" claims writer Jason Christoff. That's why it's used to extract essences for essential oil and the sterilization of medical instruments.

When consuming large amounts of alcohol, it extracts the very essence of the soul from the body. It's said that this makes the body more susceptible to outside entities with lower frequencies. This is why people often black out when consuming large amounts of liquor and don't remember what happened. Basically, the soul leaves the body because it's become too polluted to tolerate.

Because of the toxicity and pollution, the good soul abandons the body but stays tethered by a thread. This gives dark entities with lower frequencies the opportunity to take the body for a joy ride. The joy ride results in uncharacteristic and often illogical behavior. In essence, when you black out from drinking alcohol or polluting yourself, your body can become possessed by another entity. This could make sense especially when you have no other explanation for your behavior.

I share this story from MADHAV University[36] to illustrate how addiction of any kind can invite lower frequencies and vibrations into your life and can cause a host of health issues. So, as you navigate life and you wonder why you're smoking too much, drinking too much, or doing anything else that doesn't support pristine health, you're in essence creating the perfect storm for spiritual interference and health issues.

Give yourself some space to explore this question. I recommend setting your timer for a minimum of five minutes while you put pen to paper and let it all flow.

How is addictive behavior influencing your life?

_____

_____

_____

_____

_____

_____

_____

_____

_____

_____

_____

_____

_____

_____

_____

_____

CHAPTER TEN

Get the Issues Out of Your Tissues

It's time to go deeper to heal with L♥VE and release what no longer serves. Once you've taken some time to identify what's impacted you on any level, what no longer serves, you've got to get the issues out of your tissues. I'm not here to tell you exactly how to do that, but I am here to tell you that it might just be time to look at alternative healing modalities and spiritual practices that tap into the energetics of your body, mind and soul.

Some things you might consider to complement any traditional medicine or therapies (like counseling, etc.) are energy management modalities to amplify your immune system on an energetic level.

- Sound Healing (singing bowls — crystal or metal)
- Music
- Acupuncture or Acupressure
- Aroma Therapy and Essential Oils
- Massage

- Hugs
- Journaling
- Float Tanks
- Meditation (stillness, guided, and focused attention to activities you love)
- Prayer
- Alignment of your Internal Trinity (higher self, basic self, conscious self)
- Timeline Hypnotherapy
- Chakra Clearing — Balancing the Chakras
- Chord Cutting
- Toning
- Meridian Alignment
- Scaler Energy
- Inner Child Healing Work
- Energetic Clearing Sessions
- Energy Healing Sessions
- Breath Work Ceremonies
- Tapping
- Theta Healing
- Self-L♥VE Rituals
- Absolute Belief that you can Heal with L♥VE
- Future Activating, Pre-Paving and Visioning
- Spending Time in Nature
- Earthing
- Drinking PURE Water
- Eating Pure Food

Whatever you do, it's important to acknowledge and release the trauma that's held in your body on a cellular level. As spiritual beings having a human experience, we've all faced some sort of trauma. Mostly we've been taught to "suck it up," "just deal with it," "keep it to yourself" and haven't been given the tools or been taught to prioritize well-being, personal sovereignty and safety into the mix of self-care.

Rarely are the children of the world taught that our bodies are sacred temples and as such, should be treated as so. It is said that all of our mental and physical experiences permeate our very beings and are stored in our DNA. If we choose not to release this trauma or we are not taught how, disease can manifest in a variety of ways.

One of my favorite teachers on this subject is Louise Hay. She is no longer with us on the earth plane AND the legacy of her body of work lives on. Her book *You Can Heal Your Life*[6] is a must-have for your home library. Throughout my healing with L♥VE journey, I also listened to her Audible book audios of *Love Your Body*[7] and *Cancer: Discovering Your Healing Power*[8] along with many other healing meditations. In the book *Cancer: Discovering Your Healing Power,*[8] she shares how she had several reoccurrences with cancer and realized that if she didn't go to the root cause (trauma) and release that, the doctors would continue to cut away at her to remove the cancer and there would be nothing left of her. I paraphrase but you get the gist. Louise was a true pioneer when it comes to healing with L♥VE. Her work extended beyond cancer and I highly recommend her body of work as a true resource for tapping into the power of our minds and bodies when it comes to our ability to heal.

Our bodies are incredibly intelligent and when we learn to tap in to what is happening with our inner landscape, we can take measures to heal. Two more resources on this topic are *The Secret Language of Your Body*[10] by Inna Segal and *Metaphysical Anatomy: Your Body is Talking, Are You Listening?*[11] by Evette Rose. I share these resources so you can begin equipping yourself with the knowledge and tools to start healing with L♥VE NOW before you face mortality. My deepest wish is that we all start taking such good care of ourselves that we can avoid cancer altogether.

Going Deeper to Release What No Longer Serves

Here's an at-a-glance inventory of some of the definitions and benefits of these alternate modes of healing and other ways to promote well-being. These are modalities you can explore to amplify your health and create your own recipe to heal yourself with L♥VE.

We'll start with SELF, HEALTH, and WEALTH as a foundation and move into some of the specific non-traditional modalities you might consider when healing with L♥VE. Throughout the book, you will find **Spiritual Sugar Heart Sparks**. These are journal prompts to help you go deeper. I recommend that you set aside some sacred time to move through the exercises. There will be sections that draw you and that deeply resonate with your soul. Pay close attention to these sections. There are divine messages and activations that you will uncover here. On the flip side, there will be sections that are uncomfortable and that you don't want to look at. Pause and look deeper. This is the deeper inner work that is calling your soul.

SELF (SELF-CARE)

"Remember, you have been criticizing yourself
for years and it hasn't worked.
Try approving of yourself and see what happens."
~ Louise Hay

Your most precious resource is YOU. Unfortunately in the fast-paced world we live in, self-care has been put on the back-burner for far too long and for far too many, not-so-great, reasons. The bottom line, the core truth is this: If you don't take care of you, no one else will. At least not to the fullest capacity. Taking care of you is an inside job. It requires self-love, acceptance and a commitment to go deeper than the surface. It's up to you to determine what you need to heal and what will best support you moving forward. It's easy to be on autopilot and to let your own needs become less important than your loved ones' needs, your obligations to work, or any other commitments that take your time and attention.

It's time for some more **Spiritual Sugar Heart Sparks**. Set your timer, get the beverage of your choice, and write it out.

- In what ways can you take better care of yourself?
- What can you do today to support yourself mentally and physically?
- What are you doing to fortify yourself spiritually?

_____

_____

_____

_____

HEALTH

"To enjoy good health, to bring true happiness
to one's family, to bring peace to all,
one must first discipline and control one's own mind.
If a man can control his mind he can find
the way to Enlightenment, and all wisdom and virtue
will naturally come to him."
~ Buddha

Throughout my healing with L♥VE journey, I created a purple binder. The place I kept/keep all my medical records, research and notes about what I did to take charge of my health (including recipes, natural remedies, and more). The binder is thick and overflowing and it also contains my Advance Directive paperwork (the documents that authorize designated people to make the final decisions about my life).

Yes, I know that's a heavy thought and it's an important part of taking charge of your health. Today, I want you to journal about your wishes and what you have in place to help those you love make the right choices for you. Take some time to contemplate the following:

- Are you an organ donor?
- Have you completed an Advance Directive?
- If so, are copies on file with your physician?
- If not, who will you designate to make these decisions for you?
- What are your last wishes and who knows about them?
- Have you completed a will?

These are important topics to address while you still can. I know, I know, it's not a fun topic AND YET it is one that is helpful to consider so you have the right documents in place to protect you.

Set your timer for five minutes and give careful consideration to how you're taking care of you.

_____

_____

_____

_____

_____

WEALTH

"Health is the greatest gift, contentment the greatest wealth,
faithfulness the greatest relationship."
~ Buddha

I'd say Buddha lays this out nicely. We live such privileged lives that often we don't even realize how wealthy we are. Wealth comes in many forms and starts with gratitude for what we have.

- What does wealth really mean to you?
- When do you feel most wealthy?
- What is it that promotes that feeling inside of you?
- Is it material things? Health? Happiness? Family? Vacations? Luxury? The simple things in life? Something else?
- What are you doing to build actual wealth (in the monetary sense of the word)?

These **Spiritual Sugar Heart Sparks** will ignite your wealth consciousness. Set your timer for five minutes and put pen to paper and let your thoughts flow.

_____

_____

_____

_____

_____

ABSOLUTE BELIEF THAT YOU CAN HEAL WITH L♥VE (FAITH)

"Whether you've seen angels floating around your bedroom or just found a Ray of hope at a lonely moment, choosing to believe that something unseen is caring for you can be a life-shifting exercise."
~ Martha Beck

Thanks to the divine download I received prior to the cancer diagnosis, I knew I was going to heal with L♥VE. I chose love over fear and I leaned into my faith and relationship with the

Creator big time. After all, the alternative of falling into fear and accepting a cancer diagnosis as a death sentence was not a part of my plan (or the Creator's plan). Instead, I focused on love; I spent time in nature; I prayed A LOT, and I had absolute faith that I would heal with L♥VE. I also made sure to fuel my body with pure, organic food to feed my cells and amplify my connection with Source. So, today, I'm sharing what I learned on my journey in this book because it is my agreement with God to help others consider the possibilities instead of allowing fear to consume you.

I was also shown the best way to reconnect with your faith is through nature. When in doubt, get out into nature and look around. There is NO denying that there is something much bigger than you or me at play.

These **Spiritual Sugar Heart Sparks** are designed to help you explore your relationship with faith. Set your timer for five minutes and dive in.

- Do you have faith?
- When was the last time you believed 100% in something bigger than you?
- What can you do to strengthen your faith today?

_____

_____

_____

_____

PRAYER

*"In my deepest, darkest moments, what really
got me through was a prayer. Sometimes my prayer
was 'Help me.' Sometimes a prayer was 'Thank you.'*

What I've discovered is that intimate connection
and communication with my creator will always
get me through because I know my support,
my help, is just a prayer away."
~ Iyanla Vanzant

For me, prayer goes hand in hand with meditation. Prayer is extremely personal and can be carried out in whatever way you feel most comfortable.

I've found the most potent prayer is always a prayer of gratitude and thanks as opposed to a prayer asking for what we want.

When the Bible mentions meditation, it often mentions obedience in the next breath. An example is the Book of Joshua:

"This Book of the Law shall not depart from your mouth,
but you shall meditate on it day and night,
so that you may be careful to do according to
all that is written in it."

Both prayer and meditation require focused attention. Take five minutes, remember to set your timer and journal about these **Spiritual Sugar Heart Sparks**.

• What is your relationship with prayer?
• When you pray, do you give thanks or ask for what you want?
• How can you strengthen your prayer practice?

_____

_____

_____

_____

_____

ALIGNMENT OF YOUR INTERNAL TRINITY
(HIGHER SELF, BASIC SELF, CONSCIOUS SELF)

"The objective is not to chase the higher self
but rather allow it to come through the mind (conscious)
and the body (basic self)."
~ Kelle Phillips

One of the most powerful spiritual tools that I have ever experienced is the ability to create alignment with my Internal Trinity. We all have one. The Trinity is made up of our higher self (direct connection with Source), our basic self (our inner child who sometimes makes irrational decisions), and our conscious self (the thinking mind). When these three parts of the psyche are aligned, we have access to greater amounts of light and clarity.

I learned these principles from a dear friend and spiritual teacher, Kelle Phillips. She teaches this via her online programs and in particular her BlueGrid® Meditation[15] Method. I use her techniques to connect with Source and create a positive energetic force field that helps me manage my energy. You can learn more about this method at KellePhillips.com.

Set your timer for five minutes and explore these ***Spiritual Sugar Heart Sparks***.

- Are you familiar with the Internal Trinity?
- Do you feel like your basic self, higher self and conscious self are aligned?
- What practices do you have in place to strengthen your connection to the Creator?

_____

_____

_____

_____

EXERCISE

"Exercise, prayer, and meditation are examples of calming rituals. They have been shown to induce a happier mood and provide a positive pathway through life's daily frustrations."
~ Chuck Norris

One of the ways I took charge of my health and my life is through exercise. Specifically, walking. Nothing too strenuous or detailed.

I also started taking Barre Fitness classes. This is a low intensity, high impact workout with micromovements.

It took a while for me to find an exercise that resonates with me and it might take you some time, too. You have to move it or lose it. Your body is your temple and it's up to you to take good care of it. [Fun fact: I'm certified in Krav Maga self defense by David Cunningham who studied with Chuck Norris.]

Take some time to consider ways you take care of your body. Use these ***Spiritual Sugar Heart Sparks*** to journal about your relationship with yourself. Set your timer for at least five minutes and write about:

- How you currently move your body?
- How you feel about your body?
- When does your body feel the best?
- What type of exercise gives you the most energy and results?
- What else can you incorporate to get out and move?

Small steps have BIG impact.

_____

_____

_____

_____

WALKING

"Do not go where the path may lead,
go instead where there is no path and leave a trail."
~ Unknown (often attributed to Ralph Waldo Emerson)

I've never been much of a follower and that's why this quote has always resonated with me. I prefer the unbeaten path, I question everything, and have always resisted confined structure. The healing with L♥VE journey has taken me places I never wanted to go and that I hope you never end up. With that in mind, let's focus on your health.

One of the BEST ways to take care of your body is simple, free, and rewarding. Walking. Seriously, take a walk to clear your mind, elevate your heart rate and get your blood pumping. Even a quick 10-minute walk is better than nothing.

Some days I spend an hour or more walking to clear my head.

Use these **Spiritual Sugar Heart Sparks** as a guide to write about your relationship with walking. Be sure to set your timer for at least five minutes to keep you on track.

- How often do you walk?
- Do you schedule walking into your daily routine?
- Do you prefer to walk in nature, on a track, or in an indoor gym?
- What are some ways you can make walking more enjoyable?
- Have you visited a local park or gone for a walk in nature lately?

_____

_____

_____

_____

Whatever you do, get out and move.

SPENDING TIME IN NATURE

"Nature is my manifestation of God."
~ Frank Lloyd Wright

When you strengthen your connection to nature, you naturally tap into something bigger than yourself. Nature is evidence that Spirit, God, the Universe, Gaia, Christ Consciousness, (insert the word of your choice) exists.

Tapping into nature allows us to amplify our faith and interconnectedness. It refreshes, recharges and allows us to slow down to speed up. When we slow down and tap into what is and are present with the magic that is heaven on earth, we can surrender, be more connected to our intuition, and more present to receiving and following the threads of guidance from God.

Being in nature can promote:

- Increased feelings of calmness
- Increased endorphin levels and dopamine production (promotes happiness)
- Restored capacity for concentration and attention
- Reduced symptoms of anxiety and depression
- Reduced irritability
- Lowered blood pressure and reduced cortisol (stress hormone)
- Reduced feelings of isolation

Being in nature can reset you on many levels. Studies show that a minimum of two hours a week spent in nature, either at one time or over several visits, is needed to significantly increase your health and well-being.

These **Spiritual Sugar Heart Sparks** will serve as a starting point to activate your commitment to you. Set your timer for at least five minutes and let your thoughts flow.

- How often do you take time to be in nature?
- How do you feel after spending time in nature?
- What is your favorite place in nature to visit and how can you make this a regular part of your routine?

_____

_____

_____

_____

FOREST BATHING

"A nation that destroys its soils destroys itself.
Forests are the lungs of our land, purifying the air
and giving fresh strength to our people."
~ Franklin D. Roosevelt

Something that has become popular is Forest Bathing. This references a physiological and psychological practice that first emerged in Japan in the 1980s. It was developed to achieve two goals: an antidote for tech burnout and to inspire residents to connect with and protect the country's green spaces.

Forest Bathing is open-ended in practice in the sense that there is no prescription of what an individual should experience. While guided experiences exist, forest bathing can be as simple as standing in nature and engaging with the smells, sounds, and sights the area provides you.

In essence, it's just another way to spend time in nature and get grounded.

Here are some **Spiritual Sugar Heart Sparks** to strengthen your awareness of your relationship with nature. Set your timer for five minutes and allow yourself to go deeper.

- How do you feel when you spend time in nature?
- Have you tried "forest bathing"?
- How often do you spend time in nature?

_____

_____

_____

_____

EARTHING

"You learn a lot when you're barefoot. The first thing is
every step you take is different."
~ Michael Franti

Connecting directly with the earth has many benefits, especially when barefoot.

Research shows that connecting to the earth's natural energy by walking barefoot on grass, sand, dirt or rock can reduce chronic pain, fatigue and other ailments. This connection is referred to as Earthing or Grounding.

When your bare feet or skin come in contact with the earth, free electrons are taken up into the body. These electrons help neutralize free radicals that can lead to disease and inflammation and are some of nature's biggest antioxidants. The earth is a conductor of free electrons and so are all living things on the planet, including you.

The earth's energy upgrades the body, repairs cellular damage, promotes well-being, vitality and better sleep. It also stabilizes the body's rhythms, knocks down (and even knocks out) chronic inflammation and reduces and eliminates associated pain, making it the most natural and powerful anti-inflammatory and anti-aging remedy around.

Earthing or Grounding is also known to:

- Defuse the cause of inflammation and improve or eliminate the symptoms of many inflammation-related disorders
- Reduce or eliminate chronic pain
- Improve sleep and promote a deeper sleep
- Increase energy and vitality
- Lower stress and promote calmness in the body by cooling down the nervous system and stress hormones
- Normalize the body's biological rhythms
- Thin the blood and improve blood pressure and flow
- Relieve muscle tension and headaches
- Lessen hormonal and menstrual symptoms
- Dramatically speeds healing time and can help prevent bedsores
- Reduce or eliminate jet lag
- Protect the body against potentially health-disturbing environmental electromagnetic fields (EMFs)
- Accelerate recovery from intense athletic activity
- Increase negative ions especially when in the mountains or near a river or ocean

Standing on the earth barefoot or laying on the ground (grounding) can also help regulate your circadian rhythm, which can help you sleep better. Your circadian rhythm or circadian cycle is a natural, internal process that regulates the sleep-wake cycle and repeats roughly every 24 hours.

Earthing and Grounding also help you tap into the Schumann Resonance, which is basically the heartbeat of the earth. From the beginning of life on earth, the planet has had what's known as "natural frequency." The earth's natural frequency is called the Schumann Resonance, which pulsates at a rate of 7.83 hertz. It surrounds and protects all living things on the planet. Studies show that the electromagnetic field impacts the human brain and sleep and can help reduce insomnia symptoms.

These **Spiritual Sugar Heart Sparks** will help you tap into your relationship with the natural rhythms of life. Set your timer for five minutes and answer these questions.

- Have you tried earthing or grounding?
- Are you familiar with circadian rhythm?
- Did you know the Schuman Resonance is the heartbeat of the earth?

_____

_____

_____

_____

DRINKING PURE WATER

"I always say I stumbled on the information about the
poison in Hinkley's drinking water because I was sort of
stumbling about in my life at that time generally,
as a single mother."
~ Erin Brockovich

One of my commitments to me is to drink filtered water. You can get home filtration systems that purify your water and help purify you. Erin Brockovich uncovered a serious issue with water in California and let us not forget what's happening in Flint, Michigan (still).

In essence, water is LIFE. Water is of major importance to all living things; in some organisms, up to 90% of body weight comes from water. Up to 60% of the human adult body is water. According to H. H. Mitchell, Journal of Biological Chemistry 158,[34] the brain and heart are composed of 73% water, and the lungs are about 83% water.

I know that's a little technical but think about how important it is to fuel our bodies with pure water. AND then think about how many chemicals are actually in our water.

Water is truly miraculous and often we take it for granted. Pure water is vital. Throughout my healing with L♥VE journey, I spent as much time as possible at the natural spring pool at Stewart Mineral Springs in Northern California. The healing properties of this water are incredible. Dr. Masaru Emoto[21] included these waters in his studies on the purity and energy of water. They are among the purest in the world. Although the springs have changed hands and they no longer offer the hot mineral baths and the wood-fired sauna, it remains one of my favorite spots on earth.

Take some time to journal about your relationship with water (after all, it's a HUGE part of who we are).

Here are some **Spiritual Sugar Heart Sparks** to get you started. Set your timer for a minimum of five minutes and write on.

- Do you drink filtered water?
- Do you drink bottled water? (Plastic bottles contain known carcinogens that can cause cancer — do your research)
- How can you commit to YOU in choosing pure water over sugary sodas or other not-so-good-for-you drinks?
- Do you have a water filter in your home?
- Do you have access to fresh spring water?
- Have you ever experienced healing waters or do you long to?
- Have you ever taken a soothing Epsom salt bath?

Explore your relationship with water. Think about how it nourishes and heals internally and externally.

_____

_____

_____

_____

NUTRITION

"If you truly get in touch with a piece of carrot, you get
in touch with the soil, the rain, the sunshine. You get in touch
with Mother Earth and eating in such a way, you feel in
touch with true life, your roots, and that is meditation.
If we chew every morsel of our food in that way we become
grateful and when you are grateful, you are happy."
~ Thich Nhat Hanh

You've undoubtedly heard the phrase, "you are what you eat..." There is truth to this statement. Unfortunately, most of the food we find in the grocery store isn't really food (very little nutritional value and tons of chemicals — yuck!). It's said that the safest place to shop is the perimeter of the grocery store — where you'll find the produce. I'd like to encourage you to frequent your local farmers market if you have one. Or join the local Co-op (most feature organic foods).

Being physically toxic (not eating well or fueling your body with real food) interferes with your intuition. To be truly clear, you must cleanse your body, mind, and soul on all levels. If you do not, you can lose touch with your direct connection to Source and your ability to discern truth from lies.

When your body experiences processed foods or unhealthy substances like smoking cigarettes, it impacts your entire system. This is how energetic interference begins and you can become easily influenced by those who are not actually invested in your highest good (carefully examine all motives). This can result in foggy thinking, not knowing who to trust or what's real. On the flipside, taking care of your body and mind by eating pure food and exercising will expand your clarity and by being clear, you'll learn to trust and listen to your intuition.

Questioning everything, doing research that isn't mainstream, and trusting my intuition is what saved my life. While I am eternally grateful for my medical team, I'm also well aware that the influences of big pharma, the FDA and more, impact what can and cannot happen in traditional Western medicine practices. I am thankful I got clear and followed the divine guidance and threads that helped me heal.

Energetic interference and being disconnected from your intuition is how your energy field is infiltrated and manipulated and you begin to lose your power and your voice. I see far too many spiritual groomers and spiritual charlatans stealthily causing harm in the veiled name of "love and light." Unfortunately, this happens all too often but being clear can help you have better discernment to manage your energy and avoid the shysters.

One of the things I found most disturbing while doing research about nutrition and real food is most medical professionals get maybe one or two weeks of training about nutrition. This means they truly don't understand some of the most basic and powerful healing tools that we have available, pure food. In fact, one person on my medical team didn't even believe that sugar feeds cancer even though it's proven to be true. My point here is don't rely on your doctors to know what's best for you when it comes to nutrition. You must do your own due diligence and educate yourself.

For a period of time, I removed wine, chocolate, cheese, and coffee from my diet. I seriously thought doing that alone might kill me. Really. It didn't. I actually felt better than ever and I still avoid processed sugar.

I ask you to think about what you're inviting into your body. Take some time to answer these **Spiritual Sugar Heart Sparks** questions.

- How do you start your day?
- What foods fuel your body in a positive way?
- How much sugar are you eating? (Check labels — it's in more things than you can imagine.)
- Do you know what's in your food? (If you cannot pronounce it, you might not want to eat it.)

- Do you eat organic food?
- If you eat meat, do you know the difference between grass fed and grass finished meat? (Organic, grass fed and finished is always better.)
- How many servings of fruits and vegetables do you eat each day?
- Do you take vitamins and supplements to fortify yourself?
- Have you considered adding a protein shake to your diet as a meal replacement?

Be aware of how your body responds to the fuel you're feeding it and course-correct as needed. Give these **Spiritual Sugar Heart Sparks** a little more time. Set your timer for ten minutes and explore how you can set yourself up for success.

_____

_____

_____

_____

JUICING

"After doing a juice cleanse, I'm motivated to eat healthier
and not emotionally. Cleansing is like my meditation.
It makes me stop, focus and think about what I'm putting
into my body. I'm making a commitment to my health
and hitting the reset button."
~ Salma Hayek

Throughout my healing journey — one of the biggest changes I made in my diet was juicing. I honestly hadn't ever really thought about it. But as I researched what many other cancer thrivers were doing to amplify their health, juicing was a cornerstone.

I also incorporated a healthy protein shake to help me get all of my fruits and vegetables in one serving. You can learn more about this on the Spiritual Sugar website.

It's important to familiarize yourself with what is truly good for you. Eating pure food is essential. I think Hippocrates said it best with this quote, "Let food be thy medicine and medicine be thy food."

These **Spiritual Sugar Heart Sparks** are designed to help you examine how you're eating and what you might do to be healthier. Set your timer for five minutes and explore:

- How are you feeding your soul and your cells?
- Do you eat to fuel your body or to fill your body?
- Have you ever tried juicing?
- Are you aware that most juices in the grocery store and restaurants are chalked full of sugar?
- What are your favorite fruits and vegetables?
- Have you considered eliminating processed foods to improve your health?
- What's one thing you could do differently today to be more committed to your health?

_____

_____

_____

_____

JOURNALING

> *"I don't journal to 'be productive.'*
> *I don't do it to find great ideas or*
> *to put down prose I can later publish.*

The pages aren't intended for anyone but me.
It's the most cost-effective therapy I've ever found."
~ Tim Ferriss

As a writer, journaling has always been a go-to release for me. Writing your thoughts on paper or even on the computer can be quite cathartic. This is especially true if you have pent-up emotions like frustration, fear, anger or more. You can write about it and then burn the pages as a kind of release ritual.

Throughout the years, I've tried all types of journaling and I always have multiple journals going at a time. Years ago, I kept journals full of poetry to write emotions out of my system.
For a long time, I kept a journal of success to chronicle cool things I'd achieved. Looking back at the list of "successes" helped boost my mood when I was in a funk, doubting myself, or felt like giving up on life.

For the most part, I do freestyle journaling to clear my head and heart. This is a process where I write uninhibited accounts of what's happening in my life. I don't always keep these musings. Oftentimes, getting it out of my mind and onto paper helps with clarity and release. Many of these musings end up in my ritualistic burning pot aka fire pit.

Julia Cameron shares a morning page process in her book, *The Artist's Way*[50]. This is another type of free-form writing where she suggests writing three journal pages each morning, first thing in the morning and longhand (pen/pencil and paper). Similarly, to what I shared above, this is a wonderful way to release what's cluttering your mind consciously and unconsciously, put it on paper, make the space for what's next, clear your mind, and move forward.

Set your timer for five minutes and journal about these **Spiritual Sugar Heart Sparks**.

- What is your relationship with writing?
- How can you incorporate journaling into your routine?

- Do you have a journal?

_____

_____

_____

_____

You may order a Spiritual Sugar journal at https://SpiritualSugar.com

SOUND HEALING (singing bowls — crystal or metal and sound bath meditations)

> *"Tones themselves correspond with and affect specific areas of the body. The ancients understood that a simple sound could reorganise the body's structure. Sounds that are harmonious, activate the body and create healing."*
> ~ Barbara Marciniak

Sound healing is one of the many healing modalities I used on my healing with L♥VE journey. Himalayan singing bowls also known as Tibetan singing bowls are a wonderful way to raise the vibration of your body. At higher frequencies, our healing abilities are amplified. That's why music in any form is good for your soul — although you do want to be mindful of the sounds you let in. For example, soothing music like jazz, acoustic mixes and instrumentals can create a calming effect, some heavy metal may evoke more energetic responses. The point is to tune into what feels best for you and pay attention to what elevates your frequency and what brings it down.

Remember, everything is energy and while even some dissonant tones (a combination of two or more tones of different frequencies) can result in a musically displeasing sound, this is often purposeful when releasing energy on a cellular level.

Sometimes when singing bowls are played, the dissonance is intentional to help shake out unwanted energy.

Sound healing sessions typically include metal or crystal bowls. They can include gongs and other sound tools. The vibration from playing the bowls permeates the cells and creates a relaxing response. One of my favorite singing bowl practitioners is Karen Parnell of Orenda Energy Arts. I attended many group sessions with her and personally enjoyed the healing benefits of Himalayan singing bowls. Prior to my surgeries, I also experienced a one-to-one session with her. I was in such a deep relaxed trance that she didn't want to disturb me and she reported that angels filled the room. I took that as a good sign. Another dear friend, Janai shared various sound healing modalities with me like tuning forks, drumming and more.

The bowls that Karen uses are seven metal alloy bowls designed to work with the chakra system. I purchased a throat chakra bowl from her and continue to use it. I also have a crystal bowl that I play. Karen shared that just 20 minutes of sound bowl healing equates to two hours of sleep. That's pretty impressive and I know I feel so relaxed and recharged afterwards. My body literally breathes a sigh of relief after these sessions.

I experience similar sensations when I attend group crystal bowl sound healing sessions. The resonance of the crystal bowls is different than the metal bowls, both are relaxing and I highly recommend the experience.

Here are more **Spiritual Sugar Heart Sparks** to help you explore possibilities. Set your timer for five minutes and make some time to journal about this. If you haven't experienced singing bowl healing sessions, make a date with yourself to attend a sound healing session.

- How do you relate to sound?
- Do you have a specific go-to, feel-good song that you enjoy?
- How have music and sound been a part of your healing journey?

- Have you ever experienced a sound healing session?
- Have you ever experienced a singing bowl session?

_____

_____

_____

_____

_____

MUSIC

"Music doesn't lie. If there is something to be changed in this world, then it can only happen through music."
~ Jimi Hendrix

Much like sound healing, music carries a vibration that can improve your mood. I have eclectic tastes in music that range from classical to heavy metal and pretty much everything in between. It really depends on the day and what my soul is calling for. When going through my healing with L♥VE journey, I chose to focus on soothing music including music from Karen Drucker, India Aire, and Tibetan Monk chants.

The healing properties of music are life-changing.

While going through my healing with L♥VE journey, I visited Lithia Park to ground and recenter after appointments with my doctors. As luck would have it, I would often happen upon Daniel Austin Sperry[37] playing cello. The beauty of his music always struck me and I'd stop to listen (and heal). Unbeknownst to him, he and his music were a silent partner in embracing my wellness. I would sit and listen and let every note permeate my soul and cells.

Some days I would cry because the music was so beautiful and healing. After *The Silver Lining of Cancer*[3] was published, I gifted

Daniel a signed copy and let him know the impact his magic had on my healing. To this day, listening to his music is a beautiful reset and something I enjoy as often as possible. You can listen for yourself here: https://www.danielaustinsperry.com/.

I also believe that musicians are some of our most potent healers and they don't always get recognized for that. Most musicians are gifts to our world and can help heal the broken threads of humanity.

Let's talk about YOU and your relationship with music.

Set your timer for five minutes and move through these **Spiritual Sugar Heart Sparks** and journal about:

- How does music show up in your life?
- What music do you most resonate with?
- How are you using music as a healing tool (i.e., to elevate your mood, dance in the living room, background music to motivate in the workspace, live events to enjoy community)?
- Do you regularly enjoy live music?
- Have you created a playlist that uplifts your soul?

Think about the ways music shows up in your life and how you might tap into the power of music to amplify your vibration. Maybe it's time to get an instrument?

_____

_____

_____

_____

_____

ACUPUNCTURE OR ACUPRESSURE

*"I used homeopathy, acupuncture, yoga and
meditation in conjunction with my chemotherapy
to help me get stronger again after the cancer.
I also chanted with Buddhist friends and prayed with
Christian friends. I covered all my bases."*
~ Olivia Newton-John

Acupuncture is a system of integrative medicine that involves pricking the skin or tissues with needles, used to alleviate pain and to treat various physical, mental, and emotional conditions. Originating in ancient China, acupuncture is now widely practiced in the West.

Acupressure is the application of pressure (as with the thumbs or fingertips) to the same discrete points on the body stimulated in acupuncture that is used for its therapeutic effects (such as the relief of tension or pain).

Both techniques have health benefits that relieve pain and accelerate healing. I've experienced great results via acupuncture. There are some key acupressure points that also activate your immune system. You might also want to look into reflexology.

Reflexology is the application of pressure to areas on the feet or the hands. It can be relaxing and relieve stress. It's said that there are specific areas of the feet that impact our organs and body. Applying pressure to these points can help improve functionality of the corresponding organs.

Acupuncture, acupressure and reflexology are Eastern Medicine techniques that the body responds well to. Touch is vital and this attention to specific areas of the body promotes deep relaxation, recalibration of energy, and promotes a healthy system.

Use these **Spiritual Sugar Heart Sparks** to explore your relationship with touch. Be sure to set your timer for five minutes.

- Have you ever tried acupuncture or acupressure?
- Have you tried reflexology?
- Are you open to alternative modalities that relieve pain and improve your immune system?

_____

_____

_____

_____

_____

AROMATHERAPY AND ESSENTIAL OILS

"Self-care is an essential part of a healthy life.
Essential oils figure in many at-home remedies to
smooth the skin, soothe the spirit, and calm the mind.
Essential oils can be used as a part of your
first aid kit as well. They can reduce pain,
fight infections, and promote healing."
~ Amy Leigh Mercree,
Essential Oils Handbook: Recipes for Natural Living

Aromatherapy is a wonderful way to reset the senses and calm the nerves. When on my healing L♥VE journey, I learned so much about how common household products like air fresheners, scented candles, and cleaning products contain many synthetic and poisonous ingredients that are not actually good for our system. The same is true for most mainstream perfume brands and scents. I made a conscious effort to only use soy-based or beeswax candles with a natural essence. I invested in a diffuser and doTERRA Essential Oils. I regularly diffuse various scents like lavender, wild orange, and Ylang Ylang to influence my living environment. I also use essential oils topically as perfume and internally to promote optimal well-being. Diffusing oils creates a

111

warm inviting atmosphere in the home and can influence your mood. A couple of my favorite relaxing blends are Peace, Balance and Serenity. They are also a delightful addition to your Epsom salt bath. You can create a mini-spa experience at home.

My absolute favorite oil is Frankincense. It's known as a holy oil and has many uses. I take it internally almost daily and did so throughout my healing with L♥VE experience. I think the three wise men were on to something when they were said to have brought gold, frankincense, and myrrh to celebrate the birth of Jesus. To me, essential oils are gold.

Interestingly enough, many hospitals are beginning to introduce aromatherapy and oils like lavender, lemon, eucalyptus, oregano and thyme oils to benefit patients, their relatives and hospital staff. You can find out more information about this via the National Library of Medicine and the National Center for Biotechnology Information at http://www.PubMed.gov.[29] This website is one I used to research various treatments and studies while I healed.

When you're interested in incorporating essential oils into your wellness routine, I highly recommend doTERRA.[48] Full transparency, I am a wholesale distributor so I can get wholesale pricing. When you visit my link and order, I will get credit and I recommend signing up as a wholesale distributor and investing in a starter kit so you can get that discount. There is a small renewal fee each year and the savings are well worth the investment.

My direct link is https://www.doterra.com/US/en/site/lisa-manyon and I elaborate about this in a blog post on the Spiritual Sugar website.

Set your timer and dive into these **Spiritual Sugar Heart Sparks**.

- Have you tried essential oils?
- What scents and aromas bring you joy and peace?
- How can you enhance your environment with aromatherapy?

Take an inventory of the candles and air fresheners in your house and consider what could be replaced with a healthier alternative.

_____

_____

_____

_____

MASSAGE

"For many people, managing pain involves using prescription medicine in combination with complementary techniques like physical therapy, acupuncture, yoga and massage. I appreciate this because I truly believe medical care should address the person as a whole — their mind, body, and spirit."
~ Naomi Judd

The benefits of human touch cannot be overstated. Human touch helps regulate sleep and digestion, builds your immune system, and fights infections. Not only does touch feel good, promote relaxation and help with healing, various massage techniques cause blood to flush in and out of your muscles and joints, which increases the delivery of vital oxygen and nutrients. Massage is known to provide the entire body with an improved sense of well-being, it calms the mind, and helps improve sleep.

I work with several massage therapists including practitioners who bring their massage tables to my home. I highly recommend that you treat yourself to a massage especially if you've never had one.

Massage is a wonderful way to reset your system and help purge your body of toxins. Making this investment in yourself is recommended to help reset your body.

There are many types of massage[38] and for healing purposes, I recommend myofascial, rolfing and deep tissue.

- Swedish Massage is designed to relax the entire body using long strokes to return the blood to the heart.
- Deep Tissue Massage uses finger pressure to release deep tissues that are knotted and tight.
- Lymphatic Massage uses slow circular motions to move lymph fluid through the lymphatic system.
- Sports Massage is designed to relieve specific areas of pain in athletes who typically are injured from repetitive movements.
- Oncology Massage is specialized for cancer patients and uses a variety of massage techniques to promote relaxation.
- Myofascial Release (MFR) is a rolfing-based technique to treat target areas such as TMJ — temporomandibular joint in the jaw.
- Rolfing is a holistic type of deep tissue therapy usually booked in sessions of ten to work on the entire body.

These **Spiritual Sugar Heart Sparks** will help you explore your relationship with human touch. Grab your journal and set your timer for five minutes.

- Have you ever had a professional massage?
- What type of massage is your favorite?
- Is it time to schedule an in-house massage or make an appointment at your favorite spa?

_____

_____

_____

_____

HUGS

"I will not play tug o' war. I'd rather play hug o' war.
Where everyone hugs instead of tugs,
Where everyone giggles and rolls on the rug,
Where everyone kisses, and everyone grins,
and everyone cuddles, and everyone wins."
~ Shel Silverstein

This may seem like a simple solution but it's not so simple if you don't have someone to hug. The benefits of hugging include reduced stress, protection against ailments, boosting heart health, increasing happiness, reducing fear and pain and increases communication.

Family Therapist Virginia Satir once said, "We need four hugs a day for survival. We need 8 hugs a day for maintenance. We need 12 hugs a day for growth." While that may sound like a lot of hugs, it seems that many hugs are better than not enough.

The importance of human touch has become top of mind and there are now "professional cuddlers" who provide non-sexual touch to promote well-being. Hiring a professional cuddler is definitely outside of my comfort zone but for some, it may be an option. The bottom line is we all need human touch.

Use these **Spiritual Sugar Heart Sparks** as a guide to explore if you're getting enough hugs. Set your timer and start writing.

- When was the last time you experienced a hug that noticeably improved your mood?
- How many hugs to do you get/give in a day?
- How can you intentionally get and give more hugs?

_____

_____

_____

_____

FLOAT TANKS

"We will be more successful in all our endeavors if we can let go of the habit of running all the time, and take little pauses to relax and re-center ourselves. And we'll also have a lot more joy in living."
~ Thich Nhat Hanh

I've only tried float tanks a couple of times. The first time it felt kind of claustrophobic. So, if you don't like confined spaces, this might not be for you. People use floatation tanks for relaxation and to reduce external stimulation like sound, touch and light. The salt water (a solution of water and Epsom salt) is extremely buoyant, which makes it easy to float. The main benefit of using a sensory deprivation tank is to ease mental anxiety and muscle tension. The Epsom salt and water solution helps you fully relax all of your muscles and is similar to experiencing zero gravity.

Epsom salt baths[39] have many healing properties including relieve of arthritis pain, swelling, bruises and sprains. It can help fibromyalgia, ingrown toenails, insomnia and psoriasis.

I find that a nice soak in a warm bath at home with Epsom salt and essential oils is a great alternative to a float tank. You can create your own in-home spa experience. This deeply peaceful ritual always relaxes and de-stresses me leaving me feeling refreshed. Slipping into a warm Epsom salt bath with my favorite essential oil and ½ cup of baking soda is a vital part of my wellness routine and kind of like a mini vacation. Adding baking soda to your bath can help neutralize the acid in your urine, remove germs, and aid in healing.

Use these **Spiritual Sugar Heart Sparks** to explore ways you can enhance your wellness routine. Set your timer for five minutes and get started.

- Have you ever experienced a float tank?
- Do you take Epsom salt baths at home?
- Do you add essential oils to your bath water?
- Did you know that baking soda has healing properties?
- How does water and floating relax you?

_____

_____

_____

MEDITATION (stillness, guided, and focused attention to activities you love):

> *"Meditation can help us embrace our worries,*
> *our fear, our anger; and that is very healing.*
> *We let our own natural capacity of*
> *healing do the work."*
> ~ Thich Nhat Hanh

There are many types of meditation and mindfulness practices. Often people ask me how I meditate because there can be resistance to some of the more structured or silent meditations. Throughout my healing L♥VE journey, I listened to guided healing meditations on YouTube. One of my favorites is by Kalawana Biggs[30] titled, "Healing the Body, Mind and Spirit Guided Meditation."

You can find it on YouTube here:
https://bit.ly/HealingBodyMindSpirit

I believe that anything we do with love and pure intent/attention can be meditation. While I enjoy stillness meditation where you quiet your mind and sit in silence for a period of time, it took me a while to be able to do that. My go-to meditation choices are walking in nature (yes, a walk can be meditation), playing in the kitchen (there is something nourishing and therapeutic about making meals) or coloring and painting. Anything that brings you joy and doesn't take a lot of headspace can be considered meditation. I personally don't do a lot of chanting meditations but some find that quite beneficial.

I worked with a personal trainer to develop a morning ritual that includes tea time, movement, deep breathing, dancing, and journaling — BEFORE I do anything else — and that includes turning on the computer...

The key is to find activities that quiet your mind and that you enjoy to help put you in a state of peace. A meditative walk can do that while a walk to get exercise might not be as relaxing. Although, truth be told, each is a form of exercise.

Journeying inward is perhaps one of the most sacred and healing practices we can do for ourselves.

Give this some consideration and journal about how you are showing up for YOU.

Set your timer for five minutes and follow these **Spiritual Sugar Heart Sparks** journal prompts.

- How do you meditate?
- What other practices can you incorporate into your daily ritual to give you the time and space you need?
- Are there specific practices that help you anchor your energy for a more productive day?

_____

_____

_____

_____

_____

SOLITUDE

*"Whosoever is delighted in solitude is
either a wild beast or a god."*
~ Aristotle

There is a distinct difference between solitude and loneliness. Solitude is an inward journey to discover yourself, your divinity and your connection to Source.

I've found that loneliness is often a longing that occurs when you're not tapped into the essence of your soul and to your faith. Embracing solitude and giving yourself time and space to go inward is a true gift. As an only child, I am accustomed to alone time. I require it to recenter and recalibrate. Spending time in nature is one of my favorite ways to experience solitude. I find that once I've had some "me" time, I'm far more present for others. When you feel anxious or uneasy about being alone, it's a good time to look within. Might it be time for you to withdraw and go within to come back refreshed, rejuvenated and recharged? It can be considered a form of meditation.

Let's examine your relationship with solitude with these ***Spiritual Sugar Heart Sparks***.

Set your timer for a minimum of five minutes and explore:

- How are you embracing solitude?
- Are you carving out time for YOU so you have more to give?
- What would most serve you when it comes to creating a ritual of solitude?
- Are you comfortable being alone or are you lonely?
- How can you find activities that make you feel comfortable in solitude?

Take some time to journal about this and see what your soul is calling for.

_____

_____

_____

_____

_____

HYPNOTHERAPY

*"All someone has to do in order to be hypnotized or
to hypnotize him- or herself is to move down from
high- or mid-range Beta waves into a more
relaxed Alpha or Theta state. Thus, meditation
and self-hypnosis are similar."*
~ Joe Dispenza

I participated in timeline hypnotherapy sessions prior to my PET scan and surgery to help release any old, pent-up, negative emotions and trauma. Thankfully, my friend Darla is a master practitioner.

Timeline hypnotherapy involves treatment at an unconscious level and allows you to surrender negative emotions linked to past experiences and transform your internal programming. With the right, trusted practitioner, you can release old patterns and programming and rewire your brain. As with any practitioner, I suggest you do your due diligence, check references, get referrals and select the right fit for you.

There are other types of hypnotherapies and Dr. Joe Dispenza offers some powerful resources. His audio book, *Becoming Supernatural*[14] is a must-have. I also have dear friends who create hypnotherapy meditations to promote healing. A special thank you to Laura Rubinstein[16] who created a custom healing hypnotherapy audio for me, and to Matthew and Orna Walters[17] who gifted me a series of Matthew's powerful hypnotherapy audios to listen to before and after surgery.

- Have you ever experienced timeline hypnotherapy?
- Do you listen to hypnotherapy sessions?
- How could hypnotherapy help you?

_____

_____

_____

_____

_____

CHAKRA CLEARING AND BALANCING

"When all your energies are brought into harmony,
your body flourishes. And when your body flourishes,
your soul has a soil in which it can blossom in the world.
These are the ultimate reasons for energy medicine—
to prepare the soil and nurture the blossom."
~ Donna Eden

The belief in the Chakra[40] system originated in Hinduism and Buddhism and is widely recognized by energy-healing practitioners. There are seven core chakras and more advanced healers work with even more. The seven chakras are the main energy centers of the body and include the root, the sacral, solar plexus, heart, throat, third eye, and crown. When aligned and balanced properly, the chakras are said to help optimize your health. You've probably heard people talk about "unblocking" their chakras, which refers to the idea that when all of our chakras are open, energy can run through them freely, and harmony exists between the physical body, mind, and Spirit.

- Are you familiar with your chakras?
- Have you ever had a chakra balancing session?
- Do you know how to balance them yourself?

_____

_____

_____

_____

_____

CORD CUTTING

"My silver cord — the link between my body and my
spirit — was extremely sensitive. It was what
allowed me to sense dreamscapes at a distance.
It could also snap me back into my skin."
~ Samantha Shannon

Because everything is energy, it's important to have energetic integrity. That means keeping your energy field clean and clear of any outside interference. Energetic cords are invisible threads that can connect you to another person, which means it's possible for you to be "corded" or attached energetically from another person or entity.

Often these cords are attached to chakras, which can impact our heart, health, and mind. Being corded allows others to siphon your energy and life force. This is why it's imperative to do your due diligence when working with any healer or lightworker. Who you trust in and with your energy field can literally make you or break you. This is why I highly recommend incorporating a practice to manage your energy and protect your energy field. My favorite process is the BlueGrid™ Meditation (see page 92).

Journal about these **_Spiritual Sugar Heart Sparks_** and remember to set your timer for a minimum of five minutes to answer the questions.

- Have you ever felt your energy being depleted without obvious cause?
- Do you know how to maintain your energetic integrity?
- Are you able to cut cords as needed?

_____

_____

_____

_____

CORD CUTTING PRAYER

_"When it comes to soul ties and relationship cords
they are also actual living cords that are not visible
in this realm but actually do exist."_
~ Victoria L. White

You can also use a cord-cutting process like this to help strengthen your energetic integrity. This is a prayer for protection and that can help you manage your energy and maintain energetic integrity. It's most powerful and effective when you speak it out loud. Similar to speaking things out of or into existence. To get started, make sure you are in a quiet and sacred space, consider lighting a candle, cleansing your space with palo santo or diffusing essential oil. Sit in an upright position with your hand on your heart. You might also be comfortable sitting on the floor cross-legged. Speak this prayer out loud with authority.

I call pure Christ-consciousness, our collective guides and the purest light to help heal, let go, and cut any etheric cords, energetic ties, and karmic entanglements that no longer serve the higher purpose of us individually and collectively.

I ask that all cords attached to each of us that are not aligned with love, light and positive intention be released. Including: Past and present business partners, associates, friends, family members, lovers and partners, and ancestral ties connected to atonement and clearing of the land. Plus anyone or anything that is willingly or unknowingly blocking or standing in the way of full prosperity for each of us individually and collectively, including the vision for driving success in all endeavors.

I call in the assistance of Christ-consciousness, our guides, angels, and pure love and light to release all of these cords and attachments FOREVERMORE and surround each of us with a healing light to prevent any future attachments. I invite Archangel Michael to sever all cords NOW. And so it is. Thank You.

After you've used this prayer, journal about your experience with the process using these **Spiritual Sugar Heart Sparks**.

- How did you feel before and after?
- Do you notice feeling lighter?
- How can you incorporate this technique or others to maintain your energetic integrity?

_____

_____

_____

_____

TONING

"True prayer is neither a mere mental exercise nor a
vocal performance. It is far deeper than that — it is a spiritual
transaction with the Creator of Heaven and Earth."
~ Charles Spurgeon

This is a method that is said to allow you to clear, balance, and strengthen your chakras. A friend and colleague named Sharon Carne of Sound Wellness[41] offers a free, guided toning session each week. You'll also find all kinds of sound healing tools at https://bit.ly/SoundWellnessStore.

You can lead your own toning sessions by using this technique. It takes about fifteen to twenty minutes to complete.

When you're ready, let's begin.

Sit upright and keep the spine as straight as possible to allow energy to flow more freely throughout your body.

Follow along and make these vowel sounds in a gentle voice. Do not strain, simply focus on balancing and energizing each chakra. Breathe in deeply, expanding your lower stomach as you inhale. Imagine the energy and color of each breath coming into your body through each chakra. You will balance each chakra using vowel sounds. Vowels carry the "information energy" of speech, whereas consonants act to break up the energy flow. Simply put, vowel sounds carry intention and focus.

Visualize the color RED as we focus on the first chakra, your ROOT chakra — located at the base of the spine. Tone seven times with the deepest "UUH," as in "cup," a very low guttural sound just gently riding on the breath. Stay comfortable with the sound — don't force it.

Visualize the color ORANGE, as we focus on the Second chakra, your SACRAL chakra — located about 2–3 inches below the navel. Tone seven times using a higher pitched but still deep "OOO," as in "you."

Visualize the color YELLOW, as we focus on the Third chakra, your SOLAR PLEXUS — located above the navel. Tone seven times using a higher pitched "OH," as in "go."

Visualize the color GREEN, as we focus on the Fourth chakra, your HEART chakra — located in the center of the chest. Tone seven times using a higher pitched "AH," as in "ma." This is the sound that embodies compassion.

Visualize the color BLUE, as we focus on the Fifth chakra, your THROAT chakra — Tone seven times using a higher pitched "EYE," as in "my."

Visualize the color INDIGO, as we focus on the Sixth chakra, your THIRD EYE chakra — located in the middle of the forehead slightly above the eyes. Tone seven times, using a still higher "AYE," as in "say."

Visualize the color VIOLET, as we focus on the Seventh chakra, your CROWN chakra — Tone seven times using the highest pitched "EEE" sound, as in "me," you can comfortably make. Allow yourself to sit quietly for 10–20 minutes to integrate the energy. If you feel light-headed, tone an "aaaah" to bring the energy back to the heart, then an "ooooh" to bring the energy down to the sacral to be more grounded.

Once you've completed the process, take some time to journal about how it made you feel.

Use these **Spiritual Sugar Heart Sparks** to explore the process.

- What kind of shifts were evident for you?
- How did toning make you feel?
- Did you feel an energetic shift?

_____

_____

_____

_____

MERIDIAN ALIGNMENT

"When all your energies are brought into harmony,
your body flourishes. And when your body flourishes,
your soul has a soil in which it can blossom in the world.
These are the ultimate reasons for energy medicine—
to prepare the soil and nurture the blossom.
The nine energy systems include the meridians,
the chakras, the aura, the electrics, the Celtic Weave,
the basic grid, the five rhythms, triple warmer,
and the radiant circuits."
~ Donna Eden

Before my healing with L♥VE journey, I didn't know what meridians were. I learned about them when doing sessions with my singing bowl practitioner. She could tell they were blocked and realigned them. The meridians consist of twelve channels through which Qi (Chi) flows through your skin and fascia. Qi or Chi — pronounced "Chee" — is the energy flow created along the pathways that connect the acupuncture points on the body. The pathways between the points are called meridians, which also connect to internal organs in the body.

The meridians are interconnected and if you were to un-ravel them, they would form one big circle. A single meridian may have too much or not enough energy flow, which affects all meridians located in arms, legs, chest, torso and head. When your meridians are imbalanced, this can be caused by physical injury, dietary issues, mental and emotional stress, and other misalignment in the body. The meridians can be stimulated or realigned with techniques such as massage, acupressure or tapping.

A good resource to learn more about this is Donna Eden[42] of http://www.EdenEnergyMedicine.com.

Use these ***Spiritual Sugar Heart Sparks*** to journal about meridians. Be sure to set your timer for at least five minutes.

- Are you familiar with your meridians?
- Do you believe in energy medicine?
- How do you balance your Qi or Chi?

_____

_____

_____

_____

SCALAR ENERGY

"Everything is energy and that's all there is to it.
Match the frequency of the reality you want and you cannot
help but get that reality. It can be no other way."
~ Einstein

When I was looking at ways to heal with L♥VE, my friend Becky introduced me to Tom Paladino[43] of Scalar Light™. Scalar Light disassembles and eradicates the molecular bonds to the DNA/RNA of over 400,000 species of harmful pathogens, heavy metals, and environmental chemicals. This frees the immune system to restore homeostasis. I participated in several sessions to help boost my immune system.

Scalar energy is created naturally and is known to promote healing in the body with subtle energy frequencies. The energy form of scalar waves has the ability to carry information, which is why it can have a profound effect on the human body. It has the potential to pass itself onto nearby items and repair itself when broken down. Throughout the years, research has shown many potential healing properties of scalar energy, making way for 'energy medicine.' Scalar energy is believed to have limitless possibilities. It is always available, free and renewable so there is never a shortage in supply.

Scalar energy dates back to the 19th century where mathematical genius, James Clark Maxwell developed quantum physics. Albert Einstein continued this work and discovered "The Theory of Relativity." Years later, Nikola Tesla demonstrated the existence of this energy and worked to harness this energy without the need for wires. Tesla is generally considered as the father of electromagnetics, also known as Scalar Energy or, according to Tesla, Radiant Energy. Tesla believed that when harnessed properly, scalar energy has endless possibilities.

Set your timer for five minutes and use these ***Spiritual Sugar Heart Sparks*** to explore Scalar Energy.

- What is your experience with scalar energy?
- Have you studied quantum physics?
- Do you believe that everything is energy?

_____

_____

_____

_____

INNER CHILD HEALING WORK

*"After a while the middle-aged person who
lives in her head begins to talk to her soul, the kid."*
~ Anne Lamott

There are many types of inner child healing work modalities and techniques. A powerful part of healing is addressing the trauma from childhood. Sometimes these traumas occur before birth and during birth. Oftentimes, there are suppressed and unconscious memories of events that are stuck in our bodies on a cellular level. When experiencing any kind of ailment, I always suggest going deeper and looking at the root cause. Many times, it has everything to do with pent-up emotions and grief that have not yet been addressed or released. Remember, we must release the issues in our tissues to reclaim our wellness.

Set your timer for five minutes and explore these **Spiritual Sugar Heart Sparks**.

- Do you have old trauma that needs to be released?
- Have you considered that you might have unconscious or subconscious healing work to do?
- Have you considered inner child healing work?

_____

_____

_____

_____

ENERGETIC HEALING AND CLEARING SESSIONS

"Our sorrows and wounds are healed only
when we touch them with compassion."
~ Buddha

Another option to maintain energetic integrity is clearing your field with an energy clearing session. There are professional healers and lightworkers who offer this service (just be sure to check references and make sure their energy is pristine before letting them into your field). Ideally, you'll want to become so familiar with your own energy that you develop your own practices to strengthen, manage and protect your energy. See Balancing Your Internal Trinity, Cord Cutting, and Toning (pages 92, 122, 125).

"Eventually you will come to understand that love
heals everything, and love is all there is."
~ Gary Zukav

Energy healing and clearing is especially important for

empaths. A wonderful resource to go even deeper is a book by Lisa Campion[28] titled, *Energy Healing for Empaths*. She touches on some of the shadow areas of healers like energetic vampires and more.

I will mention that clearing your energy of all past relationships is vital to your energetic integrity. This is key part of healing yourself and releasing what no longer serves.

Jumana Sophia[19] offers a powerful energy clearing on DailyOM[20] called, *Break The Grip of Past Lovers*. Her book by the same name is also highly recommended. In the DailyOM[20] course, Jumana walks you through a series of exercises to release the energetic interference that past lovers have caused in your body. Remember, our bodies are temples and any sacred sexual exchange opens up to the energy of that lover and all the lovers you, and they, have ever had.

Something else to consider when it comes to energetic integrity is the difference between caring and carrying. This is a quantum physics principle that my friend and colleague, Jennifer Hough[26] masterfully shares.

The difference between caring and carrying is an important differentiation especially for highly intuitive empaths.

Caring is human nature. With practice, you can express care with empathy and understanding without absorbing the energy of the person, place or incident.

Carrying involves energy leaks and boundary issues. This often looks like codependence and taking on the weight of the world (or a specific person's situation) without being invited to do so.

Knowledge is power. When you have the pattern of rescuing or stepping in, you give away your own vital energy that you need for yourself and this can cause depletion. When you deplete your energy, this is a downward spiral. I am shedding light on this pattern so you can make a different and empowered choice.

The challenge for many gifted intuitive people is balancing the inner knowing of how you clearly see a situation and solution for others and making the conscious choice to lean back and allow the journey to unfold as it may by not rescuing or stepping in unless invited.

This is often much easier said than done and as an intuitive visionary, I understand intimately that finding this balance is the key to inner peace.

Here are more **Spiritual Sugar Heart Sparks** to explore how energetic clearing and healing can impact your life. Set your timer for a minimum of five minutes and dive in to explore these questions.

- Have you experienced an energy clearing session?
- Do you understand the importance of energetic integrity?
- Do you have your own energy clearing practices or rituals?
- Do you feel stagnant energy in your body?
- Have you ever experienced an energy healing session?
- Have you developed your own energy healing practice?
- Are you carrying or caring?

_____

_____

_____

_____

BREATHWORK CEREMONIES (BREATHING)

*"I'm convinced of this: Good done anywhere is
good done everywhere. For a change, start by speaking
to people rather than walking by them like they're
stones that don't matter. As long as you're breathing,
it's never too late to do some good."*
~ Maya Angelou

One of my favorite Women's Empowerment Coaches and

breathwork practitioners is Nicole Doherty Ananda[44]. She's a powerful priestess who harnesses her shamanic teachings to facilitate healing. I've attended several of her events and they are truly life-altering.

Breathwork is an active meditation using breathing practices to alter your mood or state of mind. Your breath brings oxygen into your body so that you can thrive. When you are physically or emotionally stressed, it can impact how you breathe. Breathwork helps to calm your stress and bring balance to your body.

People have been practicing breathwork for thousands of years, and it has roots in yoga practice. The basic idea of breathwork is to release toxins and stress when you breathe out and nourish your mind and body when you breathe in.

According to WebMD, research on breathwork is promising and its benefits can include alkalizing your blood PH, anti-inflammatory effect, and elevating your mood. It can also positively impact your central nervous system. When you feel stressed, your breath tends to become fast and shallow. This limits the oxygen entering your bloodstream. Your brain tells your body that there is a threat, and your body responds in fight or flight. It's no wonder when we're upset, a common go-to suggestion is to "breathe." Often, we are not present in the moment or paying attention to our breath and can breathe too shallowly, which can impact our health.

It may seem simple but the act of breathing is VITAL. All too often we hold our breath, take shallow breaths, and don't breathe deeply enough to get oxygen to all of our cells. This is important to YOUR health. So, let's consider our relationship with breathing and journal about it. Here are some ***Spiritual Sugar Heart Sparks*** to help with the process.

- Do you pause to notice your breath or are you too hurried to notice?
- Do you practice breathing exercises (outside of yoga or other fitness classes)?
- When was the last time you truly considered how vital

breathing is to your very existence?

- How can you tap into the power of the pause to breathe more?
- What does focusing on your breath bring up for you?

_____

_____

_____

_____

Extra BONUS for taking a step outside each morning, preferably with bare feet, and anchoring into the earth while you breathe deeply to greet the day.

TAPPING

"There are two different ways to approach shifting subconscious beliefs. One, you can bring the subconscious beliefs to the conscious mind by examining your emotions, and the thoughts behind them. Then you can tap on those thoughts that are now conscious rather than subconscious. Two, you can tap on the negative emotion even if you don't know the thought that's causing it. This is one of the terrific benefits of tapping. Sometimes we don't need to know what the subconscious belief is that is holding us back, we just need to release it."

~ *Tapping Into Ultimate Success*
By Jack Canfield and Pamela Bruner

Emotional Freedom Technique (EFT) is an alternative treatment for physical pain and emotional distress. It's also referred to as tapping or psychological acupressure. It's believed that restoring this energy balance can relieve symptoms a negative experience or emotion may have caused. The tapping process draws on the ancient Chinese practice of acupuncture, which teaches that the body's energy travels along meridian points. Certain points on these pathways are stimulated to improve the flow of energy (Qi or Chi).

The Emotional Freedom Technique[45] or tapping is a simple technique that can help you feel better quickly. It's said that tapping helps you access your body's energy and send signals to the part of the brain that controls stress. Stimulating the meridian points through EFT tapping can reduce fear, depression, anxiety, stress, negative emotion, phobias, or other psychological disorders you feel from your issue, ultimately restoring balance to your disrupted energy.

EFT tapping has roots in the 1970s when several doctors began stimulating acupressure points to help their patients deal with stress, fear, and phobias. If you want to use EFT tapping, you can perform your own tapping sequences or you can work with a practitioner. EFT tapping is easy to use as a self-help technique because you can do it any time you feel the need. A practitioner can provide in-depth healing if needed to uncover stress related to root causes that impact your present-day life.

Here are the five steps of EFT tapping:

1) Identify what you want to tap out (this is usually a fear or other situation you're ready to release)

2) Test the intensity of your issue (on a scale of 1 to 10, with 10 being the most intense, determine where you are)

3) Create a setup phrase before you begin tapping. A common setup phrase is: "Even though I have this [fear or problem], I deeply and completely accept myself."

4) The tapping sequence. Although there are 12 meridians, tapping focuses on nine meridians. Begin by tapping the karate chop point on your hand while simultaneously reciting your setup phrase three times. Then, tap each following point seven times, moving down the body in this

ascending order:

Eyebrow, side of the eye, under the eye, under the nose, chin, beginning of the collarbone, and under the arm. After tapping the underarm point, finish your sequence at the top of your head. While tapping on each point repeat your setup phrase. You may also want to create a reminder phrase that restates the issue you'd like to release.

5) At the end of each sequence, test your intensity and repeat until you reach zero intensity.

There are ample resources for tapping including audio books, instructors and YouTube videos. Dr. Joe Vitale[46] shares this technique in his book, *The Miracle: Six Steps to Enlightenment.*

Have you experienced EFT? If not, give it a try and jot your thoughts down here.

_____

_____

_____

_____

RAPID EYE TECHNOLOGY AND EYE MOVEMENT DESENSITIZATION AND REPROCESSING

"Your vision will become clear only when you can look into your own heart. Who looks outside, dreams; who looks inside, awakes."
~ Carl Jung

My dear friend Marilyn introduced me to Rapid Eye Technology (RET) and Eye Movement Desensitization and Reprocessing (EMDR) with some beautifully blessed and gifted sessions to help with the healing journey.

RET (Rapid Eye Technology)

RET works on multiple issues at one time without reliving trauma. So, for example, all of the times you've felt stuck can be released without having to revisit multiple experiences.

RET is a treatment for emotional stress. Using blinking, breathing, and eye movement techniques, RET simulates a condition of sleep known as REM, which Master Rapid Eye Technician Marilyn Rodriguez says is our body's natural discharge mechanism.

EMDR (Eye Movement Desensitization and Reprocessing)

EMDR is a psychotherapy that works on one issue at a time and enables people to heal from the symptoms and emotional distress that are the result of disturbing life experiences. Repeated studies show that by using EMDR therapy, people can experience the benefits of psychotherapy that once took years to make a difference. It is widely assumed that severe emotional pain requires a long time to heal. EMDR therapy shows that the mind can in fact heal from psychological trauma much as the body recovers from physical trauma.

Set your timer for five minutes and explore these *Spiritual Sugar Heart Sparks* in your journal.

- Do you have one specific pattern or issue that could be addressed with EMDR?
- Have you experienced REM/RET?
- Are you ready to release what no longer serves you?

_____

_____

_____

_____

THETA HEALING

*"You are the master of your destiny. You can influence,
direct and control your own environment. You can
make your life what you want it to be."*
~ Napoleon Hill

My dear friend Kathryn, who I met in meditation group, introduced me to Theta Healing. I'm a huge fan of reprogramming our subconscious and unconscious minds because I know how powerful our thoughts can be. Kathryn's unique gifts and experiences help identify and instantly transform deeply held blocks, negative beliefs and traumatic reactions emanating from the unconscious mind so you can live a conscious life with enhanced awareness.

She shares this about the Theta Healing modality:

"Over 90% of our capacity to be conscious is held within our unconscious mind. Theta Healing is a technique that allows us to look at what patterns and beliefs are programmed into our unconscious mind and how they influence our conscious mind thereby impacting our decisions, choices, and how we view the world and ourselves. Choosing to release old, disempowering programs and fears, and replacing them with empowering true beliefs of who we are, enables us to start living lives of acceptance, happiness and abundance. Theta Healing allows the practitioner to connect to the Creator of All That Is / God Consciousness and initiate self-healing in the recipient. A Theta Healing practitioner facilitates and bears witness to the process of transforming old beliefs and programming into positive, powerful new programs that one can harness to redirect their life in clear, confident, and empowering directions. The process enables us to quickly integrate the changes and initiate a new way of being in the world. It's similar to getting a new, upgraded personal operating system!"

- What conscious or subconscious thoughts do you want to reprogram?
- How do you actively fuel your mind with positivity?
- Have you experienced or considered Theta Healing?

_____

_____

_____

_____

FUTURE ACTIVATING, PRE-PAVING AND VISIONING

"You are actually pre-paving your future experiences constantly. ... You are continually projecting your expectations into your future experiences."
~ Esther Hicks

You've likely heard the saying, "You create your reality." I believe this is true. We can shape our mindset, lives, and future by future activating, pre-paving and visioning. This goes beyond The Law of Attraction. It's about intentions and action. I first learned of pre-paving from my friend and colleague Christina Merkley.[18] She has an amazing visual coaching process that can be accessed via her visual coaching Shift-It System. I still use her magnetism map and find that the visual components help anchor in desires and intentions.

When you future activate, pre-pave or vision, you are in essence placing an order with the Universe to create the life you most want. Of course, you must also take action and have clarity to help you get to where you want to be much faster.

- What are you pre-paving for your life?

- What can you begin future-activating today?
- Do you incorporate visioning in your daily routine?

_____

_____

_____

_____

MANIFESTING

> *"Attitude is the little thing that can make a huge*
> *impact in every single area in your life. When your*
> *attitude is right, you will thrive and flourish. The universe*
> *feels your attitude and you will manifest whatever*
> *attitude reflects. So let your attitude be electric!"*
> ~ The Law of Attraction

The power or your mind combined with clear intentions and actions is virtually limitless. Manifesting your deepest desires can happen at warp speed when you are clear about the outcome you want and when you FEEL it deeply.

I manifested my current living space in a matter of weeks, in an area with a 1 to 2 % vacancy rate. I knew I wanted to move. I knew exactly what I wanted in a new space. I journaled about it (including all the details, gas stove, roses, pool, plenty of space, etc.) and then I took action. I looked at two places and the second place was perfect. Ironically it had been sitting on the market for four months (unheard of in this area and clearly waiting for me). I share this to illustrate the possibilities.

- What do you deeply desire?
- Have you allowed yourself to visualize it and feel it?
- What actions are you taking to manifest what you truly want?

ORACLE CARDS AND DIVINITY DECKS

The cards tell a story...but you write the ending."
~ Theresa Reed

I personally don't play with tarot cards but I do love divinity decks, angel cards, and oracle cards. I pull cards as a form of meditation, reflection and for journal prompts. This is a sacred time that I set aside for ME. My personal ritual includes making the space I'm in as cozy as possible by clearing with palo santo, diffusing essential oils, making tea and settling in to journal. I have multiple decks and depending on what I want to explore, I might focus on one question and pull a card. I might also do a past, present and future spread to explore where I've been, where I'm at and where I'm going. Sometimes I follow the instructions from each deck and sometimes I do what my soul calls for. I will often journal about the spread and meditate on the messages. My point is, you can create your own ritual and use the messages in the cards as a journal prompt to go deeper and get new insights on what you're experiencing or facing.

As with everything, I take what works for me and thoughtfully discard the rest. One of my favorite decks is the *Divine Energy Oracle* by Sonia Choquette.[23] If you don't have a deck of your own, I suggest you take a trip to a local bookstore and browse around to see what feels best to you. Select a beautiful deck and a new journal and see what unfolds.

Here are some **Spiritual Sugar Heart Sparks** to help you explore this option.

- Have you played with oracle or divinity decks?
- How have the messages in the cards influenced your life?
- Have you considered making your own deck?

_____

_____

_____

_____

SPACE CLEARING

*"Space Clearing ceremony fast tracks the process of
making your house feel like your home."*
~ Annette Kurtz

It's a common practice to cleanse and clear your living space. This can be done in many ways. Some common practices include diffusing essential oils, lighting palo santo, incense or burning sage. Space clearing is a sacred process of setting intentions, inviting negative energy to leave and making room for positive energy.

While all of these techniques are effective, it's important to honor tradition and be clean in your practices. For example, burning sage is a sacred act and traditionally, it's not honorable to buy sage. Sage should be gifted or grown and then used in ceremony. There are many who misappropriate the use and sell it for materialistic gains. My friend Nancy brought this to my attention and shared a resource to find best practices for the use of sage. This information can be found on Instagram by following @ProtectWhiteSage.[47]

If you are in an area where you cannot ethically source sage, you may consider growing your own, checking with Protect White Sage for local sources, or using other methods like diffusing essential oil, burning palo santo or incense and even lighting a candle. Just make sure you're using organic candles because, as much as many don't want to hear this, most commercial candles are full of chemicals and substances that are harmful when inhaled. My favorite natural candles are made by a company founded by my friend and colleague Ianthe Mauro, called Objects With Purpose[31] and they are divine.

Use these **Spiritual Sugar Heart Sparks** as a guide to journal about space clearing.

- Do you regularly cleanse your living space?
- What is your ritual?
- Are you honoring traditions or misappropriating them?

_____

_____

_____

_____

PLANT MEDICINE

"And God said, Behold, I have given you every herb bearing
seed, which is upon the face of all the earth,
and every tree, in the which is the fruit of a tree
yielding seed; to you it shall be for meat."
~ Anonymous, *The Holy Bible* (King James Version)

There are multiple natural plant medicines that can improve your mental and physical well-being.

You might consider natural herbs, essential oils, or other plant medicines when selecting your divine ingredients to heal with L♥VE. If there is a local apothecary in your area, you might consider visiting and learning more. The local apothecary in Ashland, Oregon, is one of my go-to resources. They offer a magical Lung Lover tea blend that helps mitigate irritation from the smoke we often encounter in the summer months from wildfires.

You can also make your own tea blends with herbs. Experiment and explore what you like best.

I'm a proponent of medicinal cannabis that is now legal in many states. It's proven to reduce stress, promote healing, and has many beneficial uses. Rick Simpson oil is a cannabis-based treatment that has proven effective in helping with cancer. I used a blend similar to Rick Simpson oil and also used organic cannabis salves, tinctures and gummies to promote healing, reduce stress and manage pain. The Spiritual Sugar Healing Salve that I made helped my incisions heal quickly and accelerated the restoration of damaged nerves from the surgery. There is a useful docu-series about cannabis called *The Sacred Plant*.[4] It's a good place to start as you educate yourself.

Another option for plant medicine is mushrooms, both hallucinogenic and non-hallucinogenic. In small micro doses, psilocybin mushrooms can help reset the psyche.

When it comes to non-hallucinogenic mushrooms, I am a big fan of the adaptogens in lion's mane, chaga, cordyceps, turkey tail, and reishi. MUD\WTR is a part of my daily routine (it's a great alternative to coffee). If you're interested in trying MUD\WTR, you'll find information on the Spiritual Sugar blog along with a special coupon code to save on a starter kit (Note: this may change so check the Spiritual Sugar website often).

As with everything, you should do your own due diligence. I'll leave you with this quote on the topic especially in relationship to cannabis.

"Today, I believe there is no such thing as the recreational use of cannabis. The concept is equally embraced by prohibitionists and self-professed stoners, but it is self-limiting and profoundly unhealthy. Defining cannabis consumption as elective recreation ignores fundamental human biology and history and devalues the very real benefits the plant provides.

Dennis Peron, the man who opened the first cannabis

144

dispensary in the U.S., has been derided for saying that all marijuana use is medical. I would make the same point a bit differently: the vast majority of cannabis use is for wellness purposes. The exception to the rule is misuse; any psychoactive material can and will be problematic for some percentage of the population—cannabis included."

~ Steve DeAngelo, *The Cannabis Manifesto: A New Paradigm for Wellness*

These **Spiritual Sugar Heart Sparks** are designed to help you consider plant medicine and how you feel about it. Set your timer and explore.

- What is your relationship with plant medicine?
- What types of herbs, plants or mushrooms have you experienced?
- Do you use essential oils?

_____

_____

_____

_____

SELF-L♥VE RITUALS

"I'm in awe of the universe, but I don't necessarily believe there's an intelligence or agent behind it. I do have a passion for the visual in religious rituals, though, even though they may be completely empty and bereft of substance. The incense is powerful and provocative, whether Buddhist or Catholic."
~ David Bowie

Belief and faith are powerful healing tools. It doesn't really matter where you pull your faith from. I believe as long as you know there is Higher Power and your Higher Power is guided by divine, pure intent, you can heal your life. I also believe that rituals are an important part of our evolution into our truest self. I've shared many different healing modalities and tools that you can use to enhance or develop your own rituals and spiritual practice. I've also shared how I incorporate many of these things into my life and daily routine. Now, I encourage you to discover your own rituals that spark love in your heart and are your divine ingredients to help you heal with L♥VE.

Set your timer for five minutes and consider these **Spiritual Sugar Heart Sparks**.

- What is your relationship with rituals?
- Do you think rituals are important?
- Do you take time to start your day with a ritual?
- How does your favorite ritual make you feel?
- Do you enjoy the energy of crystals, the power of angel cards, the comfort of reading passages from the Bible? A long soak in an Epsom salt bath? Meditation? Something else?

_____

_____

_____

_____

If you don't have rituals, consider what you can do to carve out some time for you.

***As with everything, you will want to do your due diligence, tap into your intuition, and use caution with any of the alternative modalities I've shared.

SECTION 3

Embodying Spiritual Sugar

CHAPTER ELEVEN

7 Spiritual Sugar Principles

The main ingredient for each of these principles is having faith in yourself, having faith in something bigger than yourself, and infusing L♥VE in everything you do.

I can't give you a specific recipe to heal. No two bodies, issues, or ailments are the same. Healing is a process you'll have to do for yourself. Within this book, I've given you divine ingredients that I have used to heal myself with L♥VE. You can now select the ingredients that most resonate with you and create your perfect recipe.

In addition to the many alternative modalities, processes, techniques, and spiritual practices that I have shared, there are 7 Spiritual Sugar Principles that guide my focus in the world.

I know that love can heal everything, including YOU. I've already touched on the frequency of love and I believe it's the highest vibration on the planet. This high vibration of love is what's required for healing on all levels. The opposite of love is fear. Fear is a low vibration frequency. The lower vibration of fear can weaken the immune system, throw your body out of balance, cause illness, mental health issues, and even death.

When you align your vibration, frequency and intentions with love, anything is possible. The Spiritual Sugar Principles are designed to protect and add value to your life. Remember, every breath, every second and every experience is a true gift.

The Spiritual Sugar Principles are:
1) Fortify Your Faith
2) Fortify Yourself and Your Family
3) Fortify Your Mind
4) Fortify Your Body
5) Fortify Your Environment and Community
6) Fortify Your Creativity
7) Fortify Your Intuition

Let's Go Deeper

When I say let's go deeper, I mean it. The only way out is in and through. Consider this a treasure hunt of sorts. A journey into your soul to reclaim your birthright and energetically align with what matters most so you can live your best life. This transformation starts with you. You are perfectly capable of healing with L♥VE. Embodying the Spiritual Sugar Principles can help.

Fortify Your Faith

*"Faith is taking the first step
even when you don't see the whole staircase."*
~ Martin Luther King, Jr.

What is YOUR relationship with faith? When I speak of faith, I am speaking directly to the inner knowing that is associated with your connection to your Creator. Faith is the deep knowing that all will be well even when we have no idea how it will happen, if it's even possible, and especially when it feels like it's impossible.

There's a saying that goes something like this, "...*You've got to stand for something or you'll fall for anything.*" I have found that my faith is what creates my strength, hope, and resolve. Faith, along with my values, is the basis for everything I stand for. So, it's important to tap into your faith, whatever that might be, and hold on to a belief in something bigger than you. It doesn't necessarily have to be religious or spiritual.

To me, God is found in nature. If you're questioning whether or not there is something bigger than you, step outside and just BE in nature for a while. Carve out the time to go for a walk, visit a local park, or go on hike and see what you become aware of as you spend time in nature. I believe that nature is pure magic and the more you tap into your natural surroundings, the clearer you become and the more connected you become to the Creator.

Take some time to reflect on these **Spiritual Sugar Heart Sparks**. Set your timer for a minimum of five minutes and dive in.

- How are you letting FAITH into your life?
- Do you regularly tap into FAITH?
- How has your faith been tested and why?
- How did you move through it to realign?
- What do you believe in?
- How are you strengthening your faith?
- Have you created any positive habits or rituals to strengthen your faith?
- Does being in nature provide you with evidence there is something bigger than "you"? How so?
- What gives you hope and faith?

List all the ways that FAITH has moved you through challenging or BIG moments in your life.

_____

_____

_____

Fortify You and Your Family

"My friends and family are my support system. They tell me what I need to hear, not what I want to hear and they are there for me in the good and bad times. Without them I have no idea where I would be and I know that their love for me is what's keeping my head above the water."
~ Kelly Clarkson

We all need support. Not all of us are blessed with supportive family so sometimes we have to create our own trusted circle of loved ones. During my healing L♥VE journey, I was blessed to be surrounded with love and to have the support of my parents and my sacred sphere of influence.

Regardless of your beliefs about how you got here and why you were born into your family of origin, there are clues here that impact your very existence. Some of us are born into loving families, others are born into abusive families, many have ended up experiencing broken families, and some have never known their families. These dynamics impact us on a deep cellular and soul level. When we are loved, we thrive. When we aren't, we don't. We do the best we can to cope with the situation at hand.

This is where many trauma patterns begin. In order to fully heal with L♥VE, we have to take a deep look at what has shaped us and do the work to release, forgive, and course-correct.

The most important thing to remember when fortifying yourself and your family is it all starts with love. Remember, love is the highest frequency and vibration on the planet and when we tap into the power of love, everything is possible.

Take some time to journal about how support for yourself and your family shows up in your life.

Set your timer for five minutes and consider these **Spiritual Sugar Heart Sparks**.

- What kind of support do you need in your life right now?
- What steps can you take to create a sacred sphere of influence?
- How can you be of support to others?
- How does support show up in your life or what support do you have that you are not acknowledging?
- How can you better support yourself?

Jot down some ways you can tap into self-love so you have more to give to yourself and your family.

_____

_____

_____

_____

Fortify Your Body

"For us to become whole and healthy, we must balance the body, mind, and spirit. We need to take good care of our bodies. We need to have a positive mental attitude about ourselves and about life. And we need to have a strong spiritual connection. When these three things are balanced, we rejoice in living. No doctor or health practitioner can give us this unless we choose to take part in our healing process."
~ Louise L. Hay, *Heal Your Body*

Your body has the capacity to heal and it's important what you feed your soul and your cells. You need proper nutrition and exercise to help your body do what it's designed to do on every level. Your body truly is your temple and you are what you eat.

Unfortunately, we're not properly taught how to care for ourselves on many levels. Remember that doctors receive very little training on nutrition. Proper nutrition can help you heal. It is paramount to fortify our bodies well. Much of the food on the shelves at the grocery store is not food and we have lost our connection with the earth. Many people don't even know where their food comes from.

That's why it's vital to fortify your body with unprocessed pure food. If you cannot pronounce the ingredients on a box or a can, suffice it to say, it's not good for you. The best place to shop is in the produce isle of the grocery store or your local farmers market.

Another way you can take care of your body is through exercise. Again, even a 10-minute walk can reset your system, clear your mind and strengthen your immune system. It's important to find a movement routine that works for you. It could be walking, running, going to the gym, dancing, bouncing on a mini-trampoline and more.

I wish that as little children we were taught how sacred our bodies really are. We have been blessed with an amazing home for our souls and all too often we don't take care of ourselves. This is especially true if you've experienced any of the traumas I've outlined earlier. It's important to remember that our bodies are sacred and sharing ourselves and our energy with others (especially in a sexual manner) is a much deeper experience than society has programmed us to believe.

When we look at the principle that everything is energy, then we begin to understand how precious these exchanges truly are. There is a meme that says,

"Random Sex: When you have sex with another person, you exchange energies. If that person is carrying around guilt, shame or trauma, you can energetically absorb that. It's like going around and plugging your phone into random people's computers and downloading their files. If there are corrupt files in their system, you download them as well. Sex is a sacred act and should be treated as such."

The author is unknown but the point is valid. Because everything is energy, you pick up on the vibes of others when you're intimate.

I know that this knowledge would have been so helpful to so many. How are you fortifying your body on all levels.

Use these **Spiritual Sugar Heart Sparks** to examine ways you can take better care of your body.

- How are you maintaining your energetic integrity and boundaries?
- How can you adjust your eating habits to fully support optimal health?
- What exercise routines have you incorporated into your routine?
- How are you treating your body like a sacred temple?
- Who are you letting into your energy field and how is that impacting your health?

Make a list of some things you can do to better fuel your body on all levels.

_____

_____

_____

_____

Fortify Your Environment and Community

*"Our environment, the world in which
we live and work, is a mirror
of our attitudes and expectations."*
~ Earl Nightingale

Now it's time to take a close look at your environment. Specifically, where you live and what you choose to be surrounded by. For the sake of healing with L♥VE, this is broken down into two areas: Your home environment and your community environment.

Let's start with your home. Our homes are a reflection of our inner environment. When we choose to be in a messy space, it's an indication that there is still some deep, messy stuff going on inside our mind, body, spirit and soul. We can start this cleansing and healing by going inward and we can also start by cleaning up our external spaces. There are countless studies about this and when our space is orderly, organized and filled with only things that we love, we amplify the love vibration and attract more of that.

When our spaces are dirty, cluttered or a hodgepodge of things we don't love, our energy and vibration is lowered and we're not able to fulfill our potential. This is another place where subtle shifts make a big impact. Where can you start clearing clutter today? A resource you might find helpful is the book by Marie Kondo, *The Life-Changing Magic of Tidying Up*.[25] I found her philosophy of removing anything that doesn't bring you joy quite refreshing. Her advice to rehome, resell, recycle, or donate books that no longer spark joy is brilliant. Although, I have a hard time letting go of ANY of my books, I especially resonate with the idea of donating to little free libraries. We have them sprinkled around town in Ashland, Oregon, and they are delightful. Little free libraries are a wonderful way to share books and make knowledge available to those who might not have a budget for books.

Now, let's look at your community environment. This includes the town or city where you live, the values and principles of your community and what I call your sacred sphere of influence. Not everyone is meant for you and the opposite is true.

It's important to choose your community, location and support system carefully. I have never truly felt at home on this planet until I moved to Ashland, Oregon. I was divinely guided here to experience my healing with L♥VE journey. Of course, I had been doing deep spiritual and healing work all along but it was essential that I be here to have access to the alternative healing modalities and community to support me. I believe that this move is, in part, what helped save my life and bring me home to myself. I've never lived in a place with such a loving energy. Every time I leave and return, it feels like I'm being wrapped in a warm embrace.

Set your timer for five minutes and use these **Spiritual Sugar Heart Sparks** to consider how your environment is supporting you and how you can support your community.

- How does your environment support you?
- Are you surrounded by people and things you love?
- What can you do to create a beautiful home and community environment?

Jot down some ideas here.

_____

_____

_____

_____

Fortify Your Creativity

"A creative life is an amplified life. It's a bigger life, a happier life, an expanded life, and a hell of a lot more interesting life. Living in this manner—continually and stubbornly bringing forth the jewels that are hidden within you—is a fine art, in and of itself."
~ Elizabeth Gilbert, *Big Magic: Creative Living Beyond Fear*

We are each born with innate talents and gifts that we often lose somewhere along the way to adulthood. I'm giving you permission to find that part of yourself. I believe creativity is vital to sparking the divine in your soul. It could be writing, painting, singing, dancing, making pottery, gardening, coloring in adult coloring books, or creating your own art. The list goes on and I know you'll come up with some ideas of your own.

Reconnecting with your creative gifts is an important component of healing with L♥VE. Creativity can help you tap into and explore your childlike wonder and PLAY. One of my favorite authors is Jacob Nordby. He's weird and weird is good in my book. He wrote the books, *Blessed are the Weird* and *The Creative Cure*.[9] I highly recommend both. The words in his books spoke to my soul and reconnected me to my creativity in some truly beautiful ways. While reading *The Creative Cure*,[9] I shed some serious tears. I was grieving the lost parts of me that I so deeply wanted to reconnect to and the content in Jacob's book sparked the remembrance of when I used to write poetry and allow my passion and emotions to flow. I used to say, *"Poetry is raw emotion bubbling over into verse."* It's true and I have an entire binder of poetry I wrote back in the day. Some can likely be turned into lyrics and some probably need to be torched. At one point in my life, I recall wanting to write greeting cards. My point is that we all have talents we've buried or set aside as the demands of life take up more space. It's up to you to make space for your creativity.

I was so inspired and deeply moved by what Jacob wrote that I invested in a private intuitive session with him when I was feeling stuck about the next best steps for *Spiritual Sugar*. He tapped in and gave me some solid advice about channeling my inner child to get her message that she wants to share with the world. Much of the content of this book came from free flow writing in a journal and allowing my inner child to take the reins so to speak. Reading his books alone sparked something in me and unearthed parts of me that had been dormant for far too long. The interesting thing is I didn't even know it. You might not either.

You never know what might spark creativity. One of the ways I like to tap into my creativity is painting. My favorite painting to date is titled "The Guitar" and it was inspired by a homeless man.

It was an ordinary Monday — as ordinary as a Monday can be when you've created a life you love and can work and play whenever and wherever you want.

This particular Monday felt like a day of PLAY. I finished up a few work projects, went to a routine health exam, took my vehicle in for maintenance and decided to enjoy the beauty of downtown Ashland while I waited for the mechanics to work their magic.

On a whim, I zipped into a local spa that I'd heard great things about. There was an opening for a Himalayan salt stone massage. SERENDIPITY. So, I indulged in a little self-care (highly recommended by the way).

After my massage, as I strolled up and down main street in a fully relaxed and pleasant state, I was highly aware of what a true blessing life is and how we often take the little things for granted. I say it often but I'll say it again — the little things really are the BIG things.

I passed by a young man sitting on bench and he called out, "Can you spare a couple dollars?"

I replied, "I'm sorry. I don't have any cash on me."

He smiled. "That's okay, I'm trying to get enough money to replace my guitar. Someone stole it last night and it's really hard to make money without it."

"Wow!" I responded, "I'm really sorry to hear that. I hope someone does the right thing and returns it."

He said, "Me too. It was a gift so it was also sentimental. Are you local? I usually sit here each day and play to earn money."

"Yes, I'm local," I said. "I really hope things work out for you."

It seemed like a simple exchange AND as I strolled down Main

Street popping into local shops and treating myself to small indulgences (with my credit card — I really didn't have cash on me), I couldn't shake the request from this young man.

There were other requests along the way. Another man asked me specifically for 38 cents, which he claimed would get him off the street corner. I declined and then he playfully asked if I could take him home with me. I politely declined that request as well. I noticed that there wasn't a BIGGER why in his request for money and there wasn't a spark of determination or purpose. Also, I didn't have 38 cents and although I think it's important to address the homelessness issue, I'm not down with re-homing in my home (boundaries).

Nonetheless, I pondered the difference in energy between the two young men. What struck me most about the first young man was his desire to replace his guitar so he could make a living playing music and mind you, it appears he's living on the street. So, busking is his way of feeding himself and I respect that. I don't know his full story, I don't know how he ended up living the life he lives, but he had a glimmer of aspiration and a desire to support himself. Sometimes a nudge in the right direction is all it takes to make a huge impact in the life of another...

AND what I know from my years of managing nonprofit organizations is this — people need a hand up NOT a hand out. Even if I would have had cash on me that day, I probably wouldn't have given it to him. Though it breaks my heart to see so many people on the street in situations I don't understand, I typically don't hand cash to panhandlers.

Instead, I decided to give him my guitar.

It had been sitting on a stand in my home for years. I have no idea how to play it, I don't know how to string it, I couldn't tune it for the life of me, and once upon a time, I knew how to play three chords but I couldn't get the transition down. This guitar needed a new home so maybe this young gentleman can earn his own...

The following day I went downtown with my guitar but I couldn't find him. I tried for several days and I kept the guitar in the back of my car just in case.

Then, my Mom and I went to dinner at Larks and decided to walk down to Lithia Park afterwards. About halfway there, I saw the young man.

I asked, "Hey, did you ever find your guitar and get it back?"

He said, "No..."

I replied, "Well, I have something for you."

His eyes got wide and he asked, "Really?"

I responded, "Yes, I have a guitar for you."

His mind was clearly blown. "You're kidding?! Don't play with me," he said, unsure if he could trust a random stranger walking by.

"I promise," I replied. "I'm going to the park for a walk and I'll be back in a few minutes and I'll give it to you so please don't go anywhere."

"SERIOUSLY?! Okay, I'll be right here. Hey, can I give you a hug?" he asked. "I know I'm kinda dirty."

"Of course," I said.

We hugged. Mom and I finished our walk. I went back to my car, got the guitar and gave it to him.

It made his day. Actually, he said it made his life. What I know is, he now has the means to potentially make his own life (at the very least earn some cash and figure out what's next or not — that's his choice). I learned his name was Jay.

It would have been easy for me to judge, to walk by and not engage, to look at the gauges in his ears and make assumptions — but something bigger told me kindness was the answer. Throughout my healing with L♥VE journey, I would run into Jay from time to time and he would play me a couple of songs. He would always remember me as "the guitar lady" and told me he wished he could do something to repay me. I told him his songs were repayment enough.

I still want to write a song someday. That's why I bought my guitar. I don't think playing the guitar is in my cards and luckily I don't need to play to write lyrics.

Sometimes we have to play to our strengths and in this instance, my strength was kindness.

I recently learned that Jay passed away. That truly broke my heart. It's a clear reminder that we are not promised tomorrow. I share this with you so maybe you're inspired to tap back into your creativity before it's too late.

YOUR life is a blank canvas. You can create anything you like. "The Guitar" painting hangs in my living room and reminds me of this every day.

Set your timer for five minutes and use these **Spiritual Sugar Heart Sparks** to see what bubbles up to the surface as you write about how you can fortify your creativity.

- What are you creating?
- Are you taking time to tap into the creative essence of your soul?
- How does creativity PLAY in your life?
- What do you do for FUN that ignites that childlike wonder?
- Do you paint, draw, write or play music?
- What are some ways you can tap back into your creativity or brighten the lives of others with your gifts?

_____

_____

_____

_____

_____

_____

BONUS points for treating yourself to an adult coloring book. I recommend getting some nice Prismacolor pencils too.

Fortify Your Intuition

*"Your time is limited, so don't waste it living someone
else's life. Don't be trapped by dogma — which is living
with the results of other people's thinking. Don't let the
noise of others' opinions drown out your own inner voice.
And most important, have the courage to follow
your heart and intuition."*
~ Steve Jobs

We are all born with a deep knowing and the ability to tap into our intuition. Call it your 6th sense or whatever you like. Whatever you call it, it's a spiritual gift that requires attention to fully tap into the potential.

I was blessed to receive direct guidance from Source that I could and would heal with L♥VE. I trusted that guidance and I knew it was important to trust my intuition, also known as gut instinct, as I navigated my choices for treatment and more. I was divinely guided to resources to help me and I followed those threads.

Those threads showed me the way to new ideas and resources that Source wanted me to see and consider. At the same time, I had to use my intuition and personal discernment. For example, I intuitively felt that I should not choose chemo or radiation as a part of my healing path. Although my intuition — I sometimes call it spidey senses — is strong, I looked for confirmation that I was on the right path. I was led to watch a docu-series called *The Truth About Cancer*[1] where I learned more than I ever wanted to know about the history of big pharma, the Agent Orange roots of chemo, and more. This confirmed that my intuition was spot on for me. This doesn't mean that what I chose will be right for you. This is why it's important to develop your own intuitive abilities. The clearer you are, the clearer your choices will be.

Dreams are another way your intuition and inner knowing may be trying to get your attention. When at all possible, journal about your dreams and consider if there is a bigger message trying to be delivered by Source or your higher self.

I recommend taking some time to explore these **Spiritual Sugar Heart Sparks**. Set your timer for at least five minutes and start exploring how you can fortify your intuition.

- What does intuition mean to YOU?
- What does the Steve Jobs quote bring up for YOU?
- How have you allowed other people's thinking to dictate how you live?
- How can you course-correct to live in fuller alignment with YOUR truth and your heart?
- What action can you take to tap into your intuition on deeper level today?
- When have you used your intuition to your advantage?
- Do you look for additional evidence to back up what your intuition tells you?

_____

_____

_____

_____

_____

_____

The 7 Spiritual Sugar Principles are the basis for developing your own spiritual practice. Remember, when you tap into your faith and a belief in something bigger than yourself, you access the keys to healing yourself with L♥VE.

CHAPTER TWELVE

Develop YOUR Spiritual Practice With Self-Care

When I faced mortality, I had a peaceful calm roll over me. I knew that what was meant to be would be. I knew I could be drawing my last breath because of the cancer. I knew that I could draw my last breath from going under anesthesia for surgery. And I knew no matter what happened, I would be OK.

I cannot explain how I knew, I just knew, and receiving God Nudges was helpful too. When I received the message that I would heal with L♥VE, I gratefully accepted that possibility and knew it was a much better choice than any other alternative. I had many conversations with the Creator about this and asked to be shown the work I am to do in this world to help humanity. I find it ironic that two years prior to my diagnosis, I had received the divine download that I chose to ignore. Well, I didn't totally ignore it, I did journal about it and tucked it away. That message was "You are to write a book. It will be about healing with L♥VE. The title will be *Spiritual Sugar*."

I was not receptive to this suggestion from High at that moment. I felt overwhelmed and busy with the work I was doing with Write On Creative to teach marketing with integrity, which was another divine charge and almost an oxymoron in that industry. When I look back at that journal entry and see the other note I scribbled: "Give yourself some love," there is no doubt in my mind that the Creator was trying tell me to take better care of myself. Had I stopped and listened more closely perhaps I could have course-corrected then. Maybe I wouldn't have gone through the entire healing with L♥VE journey to release cancer. But then again, I believe everything happens for a reason. My lesson can become a blessing for you. AND it can serve as a reminder to LISTEN to your inner guidance and take better care of YOU.

Be open-minded and discerning. Discernment is paramount when developing your own spiritual practice. It's vital to your Spiritual Sovereignty and energetic integrity. Here are some things to keep in mind as you explore strengthening your spiritual connection and practices.

- Trust your intuition and tap directly into your connection with Source
- Do not give your power away
- Learn to manage your energy field
- Never blindly follow any guru, spiritual leader, healer, lightworker or religious figure
- Be cautious and aware of spiritual infiltration by those who don't have your best interest at heart (when something doesn't feel right, it's probably not right).

I elaborate on the idea of Spiritual Sovereignty and energetic integrity in the #1 International Bestselling book, *Life Reimagined* in the chapter titled, "Spiritual Sovereignty: Hindsight is 2020,"[5] I share why I do not like to focus on negative energy, and why it's important to be aware and shed light into the dark. This piece that I wrote illuminates some of the trials and tribulations of the pandemic. I share it here to illustrate how important it is to have discernment when exploring various healing modalities and spiritual practices. Remember, salt and sugar look the same...

Spiritual Sovereignty: Hindsight is 2020

When 2020 began, I felt like I was on top of the world. I had retained many fabulous clients while doing the work that I love. My *Healing With L♥VE* journey was gaining traction. I was invited to do an author reading and signing for the #1 International Best-seller, *The Silver Lining of Cancer*[3] at our local bookstore. I was in my element, surrounded by books and community, at one of the most amazing Q & A sessions I've ever experienced. Books were sold and signed. Deep connections were made. The impact of my healing story was evident, as people asked me how I managed to become cancer-free without chemo or radiation. The miracle of experiencing cancer had become a catalyst for helping humanity to heal, by demonstrating how we can reclaim our health, amplify our vibration, lean into faith, and create our reality.

Several years prior, on May 16, 2017, I heard three words that would change the trajectory of my life. *"You have cancer."* OR maybe it was, *"It is cancer."* Either way, as my ENT delivered the news to my Mom and me, I sat there soaking it in, breathing through it, and embracing what was next. I felt some disbelief and some relief... I knew it was time to heal with L♥VE. This deep knowing came from the divinely guided message, *"you will heal with L♥VE"* that I received prior to diagnosis. That felt way better than the alternative. I surrendered into a peaceful calm, while I prepared myself to follow the threads and heal with L♥VE, or gracefully make my exit. That night, I sipped on the prosecco I had purchased to celebrate "good news" and had a deep cleansing cry.

What followed was a complete lifestyle reset on all levels. Facing mortality was the moment I reimagined my life. Fast forward to 2020; after two major surgeries, lots of love, and intensive healing work with multiple traditional and alternative practitioners — I was cancer-free and sharing my story to inspire others.

And then, the world stopped. At least the world as we'd known it. The pandemic was in full swing, and businesses shut down. We were told to stay home and only leave for necessities. Humanity panicked, masks became mandatory, and the great divide deepened in historic pandemic fashion. Devastating wildfires in Southern Oregon and long overdue cultural shifts led to unrest on many levels. I call this time the perpetual unknown or unknowing. Because of the great divide between political parties, vaxxers, and anti-vaxxers, media censorship, racism, and more, truth became lies, and lies became truth.

I decided, in a moment of deep meditation, that if the world was going to end, I was going to swim. I journaled about my ideal space in a housing market with less than a two percent vacancy rate. Within two weeks, I manifested what I desired, a beautiful home complete with swimming pool, large kitchen, primary en-suite bedroom with walk-in closet, office space, guest room, and a yard with rose bushes. Interestingly, the space had sat vacant for four months as if it were waiting for me. I took this as a good sign and reveled in the vibration of my new digs. Despite this pocket of joy in my life, the world seemingly continued to spin out of control.

I lost three important people: my uncle, my kindergarten teacher, and a lifelong friend (none were COVID-19 related but were devastating losses nonetheless). World health dictated social distancing; hugs became acts of rebellion. Depression was on the rise, including my own. On multiple levels, I simultaneously experienced heartbreak and heart opening. I felt as though I had lost my magic. I experienced my first and only bout of TMJ, necessitating physical therapy to loosen my jaw. I could barely open my mouth (another form of trying to suppress my voice and not fully being valued, heard, or seen, perhaps).

It was everything I could do to maintain my sanity, peace of mind, and faith. My stress levels were high, and this was especially concerning for me. As a cancer thriver, I know the importance of energetic integrity and taking care of the body, mind, and spirit. All are paramount to BEing healthy and at peace. For the most part, I stayed in my little bubble. Despite the slight sense of security gained by tapping into conveniences like Instacart grocery delivery, I felt the collective fear permeating my sacred sphere of influence. As a highly intuitive empath, it takes extra effort for me to manage my energy and not take on the weight of the world.

In times of unrest, when collective fear permeates the atmosphere, the perpetual unknowing hangs thick in the air, showering us with doubt and sucking the hope and joy from our hearts. It is too easy to give our voice and power away, without even realizing it. When seeking, we often turn to gurus, healers, teachers, coaches, mentors, and even well-meaning friends who don't hold the key to our inner truth. I did everything I could to maintain my energetic integrity, including deep healing work with some trusted and not so trusted healers. I learned difficult lessons about allowing others into my energy field. These lessons rolled over into 2021 and my sacred sphere of influence.

I navigated these life-altering experiences seeking support from healers and lightworkers, some of whom were spiritual groomers and spiritual charlatans/shysters. I was clearly shown how many healers manipulate the vulnerability of others for their gain. I experienced breaches of trust, and boundaries were crossed. One healer attempted to play a fatherly role in my life, began to gain trust, and started pushing additional sessions when they were not necessary. My struggle with depression was shared, without permission, by a trusted friend to a partner practitioner, who did not have my best interest at heart. This person tried to sabotage my work and my health, and project on to me that "almost all people suffering from depression are not living their purpose." This person systematically drove a wedge between my previously trusted friend and me, in the guise of "love and light."

What I discovered is that the truth of those healers was not my truth. I was shown how they were trying to manipulate others. I realized that things get wonky when I become separated from my direct connection with my higher self and God. Thankfully, I came full circle back to my faith. But, not before experiencing powerful lessons, including the importance of energetic integrity and the damage energetic interference can cause.

Not all things are as they seem, and many times stories are conjured, influenced, and shaped by half-truths that have been projected to impact your worldview. Spiritual charlatans/shysters and spiritual groomers are often self-proclaimed healers who promote themselves as trusted advisers and share many of the same patterns. They lack boundaries, exhibit unhealthy dark undertones and deep personal agendas both consciously and subconsciously. They are masters of cloaking their true essence shrouded in the guise of "love and light" while imparting great harm on those they claim to serve.

It's now clear to me that when organizations, "healers" with their interests and beliefs, begin to stealthily infiltrate my sacred space, trying to influence me in manipulative ways, it's time to take a step back. When experiencing people and situations like this, I've learned to question everything, break the trance, challenge the status quo, and engage in critical thinking. This is my personal framework for discernment and I want you to have it too.

By BEing fully aligned with my truth, intuition, faith, and direct connection with Source (God, the Universe, Creator, Gaia, or whatever term resonates), the veil was lifted, and it all became crystal clear and certain. I simultaneously regained my energetic integrity and Spiritual Sovereignty. I reclaimed my essence, and I can feel the magic of life again. I gave myself grace when releasing people, places, and things that no longer serve. I learned to let go and allow the journey to unfold for others without my input or influence.

What I wish for YOU today is Spiritual Sovereignty. May you hold fast to your ability to connect with your higher self directly through the Creator. May you embrace only pure love. May you break through the illusions of guruism, losing your voice and giving your power away.

Do not let others influence or derail your purpose. Trust your faith. It is your direct connection with Source that leads to Spiritual Sovereignty. This is when you know you've come home to yourself and have finally tapped into Spiritual Sugar, the inner sweetness of your soul where you can heal yourself with L♥VE.

Reflect on these questions.

- Where are you giving your power and your voice away?
- How can you trust your intuition more?
- In what ways are you deepening your faith to strengthen your Spiritual Sovereignty?

_____

_____

_____

_____

_____

Not All Spiritual Things are Holy

You may recall me writing that not all things that are spiritual are holy. This is another universal truth and the spiritual community has become overrun with shysters, charlatans, spiritual groomers and energy vampires. This is why tapping into your intuition and learning techniques to maintain your energetic integrity are crucial. A meditation that I mentioned previously and that I incorporate into my personal practice is called The BlueGrid™ Method. This meditation fortifies my energy field, aligns my internal Trinity (basic self, conscious self, and higher self), and amplifies my intuition.

I've been incorporating this process into my practice for over a decade and I've noticed that when I don't do this daily, there are definitely openings in my energy field and my discernment can become cloudy. I'm a firm believer that as we tap into our higher selves, our intuition is strengthened. And I find that a direct connection to the Creator is more powerful than diluted connections with unknown guides. I do call upon angels and ascended masters for additional assistance.

Bringing It All Together

As you consider all of the information I've shared with you here, I want you to take what works for you and set aside what doesn't resonate. You may or may not revisit those sections of the book but chances are, when you do, you'll be open to what is shared. Things have a way of presenting themselves when you are ready to receive.

I've given you a lot to consider and many divine ingredients to heal yourself with L♥VE. It's up to you to create your own recipe and design a life you love. Some of the most powerful things I did to heal myself with L♥VE and continue to do include:

- Surrendering and following the threads with complete faith
- Reconnecting and strengthening my faith
- Appreciating nature
- Leaning into love
- Practicing gratitude
- Realizing that every second is a gift
- Questioning everything

Every person, every body, and every ailment is different. That's why there isn't a one-size-fits-all solution or cure for anything in this world. It's up to YOU to find out what works best for you and do more of that.

It's my sincere wish that what I've shared in this book will inspire you to commit to YOU and make your health your #1 priority. Choose the ingredients to create your personal recipe to heal yourself with L♥VE.

CHAPTER THIRTEEN

Going Even Deeper

Following are more **Spiritual Sugar Heart Sparks**, also known as journal prompts to help anchor in your truth.

PERFECTION AND IMPERFECTION

"In nature, nothing is perfect and everything is perfect.
Trees can be contorted, bent in weird ways,
and they're still beautiful."
~ Alice Walker

In our society, there is a push for perfection and for creating the proverbial perfect life. AND, when we peel back the layers, we know NOTHING is perfect but everything is perfectly fine. I have found my greatest comfort in nature, feeling the energy of the earth, and marveling at the beauty of LIFE. Nature has shown me that perfection is unattainable. As you slow down, you'll discover that all too often you are rushed, and you likely take the world and your life for granted.

Today, I invite you to look at the perfection in imperfection.

Grab your journal, a nice pen or pencil, a cup of tea and use these **Spiritual Sugar Heart Sparks** to consider:

- What seems imperfect in your life right now?
- How can you flip the script to see the perfection in the imperfection?
- How does spending time in nature help you tap into the perfection of the simple things in life.
- What seems perfect in your life right now?
- Do you see the perfection in imperfection?

Remember, every second of this life is a blessing. How are you celebrating your gifts?

_____

_____

_____

_____

BLOOM

"I hope you will go out and let stories happen to you, and that you will work them, water them with your blood and tears and your laughter till they bloom, till you yourself burst into bloom."
~ Clarissa Pinkola Estes

We don't always get to choose our circumstances but we do get to choose how we respond. That's why it's important to bloom where you are planted no matter what this lifetime deals you.

Today, I ask you to set your timer for at least five minutes and use these **Spiritual Sugar Heart Sparks** as a guide to consider:

- How are you responding to your circumstances?
- What actions can you take to create what you truly desire?
- How are you letting stories shape you?
- What stories are you telling that could be rewritten to bring you greater joy?
- What does the statement, "Bloom where you are planted" bring up for you?

Our lives and our reactions to what life brings our way shape who we are. We have the ability to shift our mindset and perspective. What do you choose? What makes your heart and soul blossom in joy?

_____

_____

_____

_____

I AM

"God isn't present in the past or future.
The great 'I Am' is in the present moment.
When I claim that presence,
I can get through anything today."
~ Regina Brett

I AM presence is known as your true self. Some refer to this as God. What I've found to be true is that there is great power in creating I AM statements to claim what you want in your life as if it already exists and is in your reality. This is also referred to as speaking things into existence. This is a practice many of my tapped in, sacred sphere of influence and I use to manifest what we deeply desire. The power of I AM statements can be quite profound.

During my healing journey, some of my most powerful I AM statements were:

- I am healthy and healed
- I am whole
- I am worthy
- I am light
- I am love, loved and loving

I know that many dismiss these practices as hocus pocus or nonsense. I am here to tell you that combining I AM statements with deep intention ceremonies, where I spoke my healing into existence, helped save my life.

Even if you are skeptical, I invite you to carve out some time with your journal to map out some I AM statements of your own. When we give time and attention to our deepest desires, we can manifest them. To manifest your I AM statements, you'll need to take action to embody what you want to BE, DO, FEEL, and HAVE.

I invite you to set your timer and give your I AM statements some attention using these **Spiritual Sugar Heart Sparks** as a guide.

- What do you most deeply desire?
- Have you given yourself permission to feel into that and given energy to actualizing it (whatever IT is)?
- What do you wish to manifest with your I AM statements?

Write your list of I AM statements and speak them out loud as if they already ARE.

_____

_____

_____

_____

BURNING BRIDGES

"Sometimes you get the best light from burning a bridge."
~ Don Henley

When you're on any healing journey, there are bridges to cross and even bridges to burn. As you evolve spiritually, you cannot go back to who you were for so many reasons. The biggest reason is self-love and doing what's in your best interest.

Another quote that speaks to this is from Neale Donald Walsch,[13] *"Understanding replaces forgiveness in the mind of the master."* In one of his books, he shares that you don't necessarily have to forgive anyone. I think that's an interesting concept. I'd like to add that you can release people from your life, forgive them from afar and still deny access. One of my personal mantras is *"Forgiven — Access Denied."* This is my rule of thumb anytime someone shows me who they really are: I believe them, release them, and don't allow them into my energy field. It's not always necessary to have any contact or communication for closure. You decide what's best for you.

Another way to forgive and move on is with the Hawaiian ho'oponopono prayer. This is an easy and powerful soul healing practice that my friend Yvonne first shared with me. Dr. Joe Vitale also shares this process. By repeating these four phrases you can transmute the charge of a situation and dissolve it with forgiveness from afar. "I'm sorry. Please forgive me. Thank you. I love you."

Set your timer for five minutes and use these *Spiritual Sugar Heart Sparks* to ask yourself:

- Who and what is most supporting my relationship with myself?
- Who and what is contributing to me being the healthiest I can be?

- Who and what is helping me embrace my relationship with money and build more wealth? (Remember, wealth isn't always about money and it's usually related to worth and what we value most.)
- What is no longer serving me and is coming up to let go?
- How can I align with only that which serves my highest good?

Once you've identified the areas that are uplifting your personal evolution, take some time to examine what's not working. Make a list and consider making changes that do work for you. It's stretchy but it's so good for the soul. Because when we identify what's not working, we eliminate it and make space for even more of what we do want.

What will you let go of today?

_____

_____

_____

_____

_____

ENERGY AND INTENTION

> *"Where Attention goes Energy flows;*
> *Where Intention goes Energy flows!"*
> ~ James Redfield

Throughout my healing with L♥VE journey, I paid a lot of attention to energy and intention. The key areas that were top of mind included self, health, and wealth. I had to reset my relationship with myself and commit to me to heal with L♥VE. I didn't give myself another choice. I got a clear message from the Creator that said, "Your number one priority has to be YOU." Clearly, I had to focus on my health first, which too few of us do. And, I had to face my money story square in the eyes again to think about wealth. One thing I learned is that the proverbial three-month savings cushion that finance experts recommend, is not really enough for a real emergency. Most of the non-traditional modalities that I incorporated into my healing journey were not covered by insurance. I invested in massages, healing sessions, juicing and organic food and all of that adds up. That's why one of the core areas I invite you to redefine in your life is your relationship with wealth.

Here are some **Spiritual Sugar Heart Sparks** to get you started. Set your timer, grab your journal and your favorite writing tool and dig in.

- When you think of wealth, what comes up for you?
- Are you actively building wealth?
- How can you leverage money to work for you?
- Are you making sure to pay yourself first (meaning putting money in savings, drawing an actual paycheck from your business, and investing in a retirement fund?)
- How can you foster a better relationship with money?

_____

_____

_____

_____

_____

HEART OPENINGS

"The most beautiful things in the world cannot be seen or even touched, they must be felt with the heart."
~ Helen Keller

When we tap into our feelings and experience heart openings, a whole new world opens for us. All too often we hide behind a protective wall built from pain, fear, old patterns, and antiquated stories we tell ourselves that are not in our best interest and often aren't true.

This quote from Helen Keller above says it all. Close your eyes for a minute.

Take a deep breath. Now, set your timer and use these **Spiritual Sugar Heart Sparks** to journal and ask yourself:

- What am I feeling in my heart?
- What matters most to me in this moment?
- How can I experience a greater heart opening to let more love flow?
- What will make me FEEL into what's best for me?
- How can I open my heart to receive more of the goodness of life?

Be present in the moment and allow yourself to FEEL deeply. This is the doorway to pure love and L♥VE is the only answer.

_____

_____

_____

_____

REFLECTIONS

"There are three methods to gaining wisdom.
The first is reflection, which is the highest.
The second is limitation, which is the easiest.
The third is experience, which is the bitterest."
~ Confucius

When I faced mortality, reflection became a huge part of the healing journey. This quote spoke to me and it made me think of you.

I remember so clearly sitting in my office wondering if I was being delusional and if my body was truly giving out on me. I wouldn't allow limiting beliefs or fear get in my way. Instead, I reflected on the situation and chose to believe I would heal with L♥VE. I thought about all the things I'd already achieved in this lifetime and some things I'd really like to experience and I thanked God for all of it. Facing mortality was a choice point and I chose life. At the same time, I was resigned to the divine plan and if that meant my life was over, I was still extremely grateful. I also made a commitment to make the necessary changes to save myself.

It's my hope that you can reflect upon your life now to make changes that prevent you from ever having to go through what I went through.

As you think about reflections, both figuratively and literal-ly, use these **Spiritual Sugar Heart Sparks** to journal about changes you can make now to improve your well-being.

- How are you taking care of you?
- What routines do you need to incorporate to amplify your health?
- Are you tapping into your creativity and having FUN?

Make a list of things you want to experience more of and start participating in life in ways that bring you joy.

_____

_____

_____

_____

_____

JOY

"We are shaped by our thoughts; we become what we think.
When the mind is pure,
joy follows like a shadow that never leaves."
~ Buddha

Our thoughts are powerful. The Law of Attraction states that thoughts become things. It's easy to slip into a spiral of despair when things aren't going your way. AND you have the power to redirect the downward spiral when you focus on joy.

That's why I choose to focus on the positive aspects of LIFE. I do little things each day to create joy in my life. This can be as simple as pausing to take a break and brew a warm cup of tea, going for a walk, journaling, listening to music, visiting with a friend and the list goes on.

Use these **Spiritual Sugar Heart Sparks** to explore how you can bring more joy into your life.

- How do you reset your mindset when you get into a funk?
- When you feel yourself spiraling (and we all do this), how quickly can you shift that energy?
- What are some things you can do in this moment to bring you joy?

_____

_____

_____

_____

_____

LIGHT

"Darkness cannot drive out darkness; only light can do that.
Hate cannot drive out hate; only love can do that."
~ Martin Luther King, Jr.

With all the negativity and dark energy in the world, it's important to focus on L♥VE — not hate. It takes a lot of energy to choose responses that are empowering. It's human nature to be impacted by bad news and things we don't agree with. Reactions to world issues, the negativity of others, and even the impact of electronics and social media can bring us all down.

Here's what I do to amplify the light in my life. I acknowledge issues that have a negative charge and I send them love. I consider ways I can make a difference in that specific instance and if I cannot, I let it go with prayer. I also find the light is brighter when I spend time in nature and it helps ground me.

I love how Martin Luther King, Jr. references the importance of love and light in the quote above.

Consider these ***Spiritual Sugar Heart Sparks*** as you take five minutes to journal about your relationship with the light.

- How do you focus on light and release the dark?
- How do the words of Martin Luther King, Jr. impact you?
- What are you doing to make the world a better place for you and for others?
- How do you shine your light in the world?
- How do you differentiate between light and dark energies?

_____

_____

_____

_____

_____

WORRY

"Worrying is praying for things you don't want."
~ Donna Stoneham, Ph.D.

My main focus during this journey was to stay positive. This meant that I also needed my sacred sphere of influence to be on board with my dedication to absolute faith that I would heal with L♥VE. I knew this was taking a big toll on my parents and I sent them a card that said (among other things), "Remember, worrying is literally a prayer for what you don't want." My Mom told me that my Dad got teary when he read those words and said, *"Now I'm worried about worrying..."* THIS is something to consider. Take some time to journal about worry.

- What are you worrying about that can be given over to God, Angels, Guides, or your chosen Higher Power?
- Instead of worrying, how can you focus on positive outcomes?
- How does worry show up in your life?
- Have you considered focusing on gratitude for what you have instead of worrying about what you don't?
- What's your biggest worry and how can you release that?

Take ONE area of your life that is a concern and create a positive affirmation to focus on the outcome you most desire.

_____

_____

_____

PURPOSE

*"I truly believe that everything that we do and
everyone that we meet is put in our path for a purpose.
There are no accidents; we're all teachers —
if we're willing to pay attention to the lessons we learn,
trust our positive instincts and not be afraid to take risks
or wait for some miracle to come knocking at our door."*
~ Marla Gibbs

Being faced with mortality prompted me to think about what really matters. It caused me to wonder what would happen if this was just it. I sat in inquiry about the possibility. I wondered if this was the end, would I have achieved everything I wanted to achieve in life. I wondered if I was going to die… I chose to live. I leaned into my faith because I knew God had a bigger purpose for me.

Everything in life has purpose and there is a purpose for everything that happens in your life. I believe that one of your greatest purposes is simply being you.

Here are some **Spiritual Sugar Heart Sparks** to help you examine:

- What is your purpose?
- What has purpose in your life?
- What is the most purposeful thing you can do right now?
- Do you believe that everything in life has a purpose?
- How can you tap into your faith to be guided to your purpose?

_____

_____

_____

THE UNKNOWN

*"A dream is your creative vision for your life in the future.
You must break out of your current comfort zone and become
comfortable with the unfamiliar and the unknown."*
~ Denis Waitley

The only thing constant in life is change and we never know when and how change will occur. This is where the unknown comes into play. My healing with L♥VE journey was all about the unknown for me. Many thought I was crazy when I told them I was going to heal with L♥VE. I had to lean into my faith and trust that the God Nudges I received were real. There is no magic formula for leaning into faith, navigating change or braving the unknown. It's my intention that this book provides you with some tools that will help.

Here are some **Spiritual Sugar Heart Sparks** designed to help you consider times where you faced uncertainty and had to embrace the unknown. Set your timer for five minutes and write about:

- How do YOU deal with the unknown?
- Are you firmly anchored into faith? Do you tap into trust? Your intuition? Or do you give into fear?
- How did you navigate not knowing?
- What have you tapped into to get you to the other side of fear?
- How can you become comfortable with the unknown and not knowing everything?

_____

_____

_____

_____

_____

Dedicated to YOU

This is a poem that was given to me by a friend when I was fourteen years old. We were navigating the transition from elementary and middle school to high school and so many other teenage transitions. I was personally struggling with issues that I didn't share with anyone — not even my family. Keeping emotions bottled up inside is never the answer and sometimes we don't have the tools to cope any other way.

What I learned over time is that any trauma left unaddressed will stay in your body, get trapped in your cellular memory and can cause illness. I believe this is partially what happened with the cancer diagnosis I received. I'm not going to reveal the details because not all stories need to be told but they do need to be addressed with professional help if you want to move past them. At that time in my life, this poem was a timely gift. I've kept it all these years and it's a good reminder of the importance of being sovereign in your own energy and focusing on self-love. I dedicate this to you and the inner child in all of us, may we all find the divine ingredients to heal with L♥VE once and for all.

After a While

"After a while you learn the subtle difference
Between holding a hand and chaining a soul,
And you learn that love doesn't mean leaning
And company doesn't mean security,
And you begin to learn that kisses aren't contracts
And presents aren't promises,
And you begin to accept your defeats
With your head up and your eyes open
With the grace of a woman, not the grief of a child,
And you learn to build all your roads on today,
Because tomorrow's ground is too uncertain for plans,
And futures have a way of falling down in mid-flight
After a while you learn
That even sunshine burns if you get too much.
So you plant your own garden and decorate your own soul,
Instead of waiting for someone to bring you flowers.
And you learn that you really can endure…
That you really are strong,
And you really do have worth.
And you learn and learn…
With every goodbye you learn."

~ Veronica Shoffstall

This is Your Life and You are the Star

I've shared many resources that you can explore and it all boils down to choice points. I believe with all my heart that we can heal with L♥VE and that it's up to each of us to harness the power within. What will you choose?

Reach for the Stars

Listen well and remember my friend,
The world is in the palm of your hand.
There are no limitations to what you can do,
The choice is yours, it's all up to you.
Set your goals high and reach for the stars,
Strive for success no matter where you are.
You determine your future, no one else can,
Prove your worth by taking a stand.
Be your own person and do what you wish,
No one should expect any more than this.
Don't let others limit the opportunities that await,
Become what you want before it's too late.
It's all up to you, so be who you are,
This is your life and you are the star.

By: Lisa Swafford Manyon,
first published in the AHS 1987 Yearbook
(Dedicated to my soul sisters from Humboldt)

Afterword

Nothing I have ever read is quite like this book. Nothing. This is more than a look at the experience of someone who has healed from cancer. As important, insightful, and deeply impacting as that aspect of this text is, I experienced it as even more than that.

What's contained here is a veritable Encyclopedia of Tools to Change Life for the Better—whether one has been dealing with cancer, some other disease, or no physical illness at all. As such, it is a treasure chest.

So don't put this book down where you may seldom place your eyes on it again. Put it within quick and easy reach, because you'll want to refer to its passages and sections often.

Wait. That's the perfect word. This is a *Reference Book*, with more information than I've ever seen in any one place on the many approaches to life improvement that we've all heard of, wanted to know more about—and *needed* to know more about when life was besetting us.

I can't imagine how much time it took Lisa Manyon to find, research, study, and learn about all the modalities she's explored here, but we all owe her our huge thanks for saving *us* this time. Talk about turning her challenge into our gain.

And isn't that what all great Messengers have done?

So now, you can become a messenger, too. Tell everyone you know about the remarkable resource you have found here.

What Lisa has accomplished here totally personifies the words in the following work by the American poet Em Claire.

(Full disclosure: Em Claire [49] is my beloved life partner and wife. I find this poem from her published works to be a wonderfully suitable way to describe, at the close of this book, the gift that Lisa has given us here...and that you are now invited to pass on to others.)

194

SOUL LANGUAGE

Speak in a Soul Language
so that Everyone can hear.

Restore this story of humanity,
with a
presence so precious
no words
could give it definition.

Practice loving so openly,
that the word for tears
becomes
"ocean"
and
the School of Compassion
is this
World's Greatest Institution.

Let no one walk alone
on this journey that is
Ours
to share:

Speak in a Soul Language,
so that Everyone can hear.

By: Em Claire[49], American Poet https://emclairepoet.love/

Here's to healing with L♥VE,

Neale

Neale Donald Walsch, author of the *Conversations With God* series of books, is a modern-day spiritual messenger whose words continue to touch the world in profound ways. With an early interest in religion and a deeply felt connection to spirituality, Neale spent the majority of his life thriving professionally, yet searching for spiritual meaning before experiencing his now-famous conversation with God. The *Conversations With God* series of books that emerged from those encounters has been translated into 37 languages, touching millions and inspiring important changes in their day-to-day lives. http://nealedonaldwalsch.com/

About the Author

Lisa Manyon is the author of *Spiritual Sugar*. She is known as the business marketing architect and is president of Write On Creative® and Write On Creative Publishing. She pioneered the values-based Challenge. Solution. Invitation™ communication framework to create marketing messages with integrity by focusing on PASSION points. Her strategies are known to create

million-dollar results. She is a cancer thriver who believes in healing with L♥VE.

Lisa is available for book signings and readings of *Spiritual Sugar* and/or the #1 International Bestselling book, *The Silver Lining of Cancer*,[3] for speaking engagements with a focus on women's wellness and spiritual health.

Lisa also hosts private, holistic workshops and retreats for individuals and groups. She lives in magical Ashland, Oregon. Call 1.866.620.1428 to schedule a speaking engagement, group presentations to your organization, or to order bulk quantities of *Spiritual Sugar* and personalized copies of *The Silver Lining of Cancer*,[3] or for general inquiries. Visit https://SpiritualSugar.com for updates.

Resources and Sources

The best way to stay up to date on all things Spiritual Sugar is to visit the website at https://SpiritualSugar.com. Be sure to check the Blog for specific products, services, and recommendations.

Below is a list of resources and sources mentioned throughout that book.

1. The Truth about Cancer: A Global Quest, An Original Docu-Series at https://bit.ly/CancerTHETruth, https://go2.thetruthaboutcancer.com/agq-encore/episode-1/ https://go2.thetruthaboutcancer.com/agq-encore/episode-2/

2. Turner PhD, Kelly A. *Radical Remission: Surviving Cancer Against All Odds,* Reprint Edition, HarperOne, 2015, Amazon: http://amzn.to/2BCOuT5

3. Ehman, Tracey. *The Silver Lining of Cancer: 13 Courageous Women Share Their Inspirational Stories After a Life-Changing Diagnosis,* Women Speakers Association, 2019, Amazon: https://www.amazon.com/dp/B09WVH9KCY

4. The Sacred Plant docu-series

5. Joy, Linda. *Life Reimagined: Women's Stories of Hope Resilience and Transformation,* Inspired Living Publishing, 2021, Amazon: https://www.amazon.com/dp/1732742545

6. Hay, Louise. *You Can Heal Your Life,* Illustrated Edition, Hay House, 1984, Amazon: https://www.amazon.com/dp/0937611018

7. Hay, Louise. *Love Your Body: A Positive Affirmation Guide for Loving and Appreciating Your Body,* Audible Audiobook, Hay House, 2006. Amazon: https://www.amazon.com/audiobook/dp/B000LMPDMC/

8. Hay, Louise. *Cancer: Discovering Your Healing Power,* Hay House, 2004, Audible: https://www.audible.com/pd/Cancer-Audiobook/B002V0K8CC

9. Nordby, Jacob. *The Creative Cure: How Finding and Freeing Your Inner Artist Can Heal Your Life*, Hierophant Publishing, Amazon: https://www.amazon.com/dp/195025304X

10. Segal, Inna. *The Secret Language of Your Body: The Essential Guide to Health and Wellness*, Beyond Words; Reprint edition, 2010, Amazon: https://www.amazon.com/dp/1582702608

11. Rose, Evette. *Metaphysical Anatomy: Your Body is Talking, Are You Listening?* CreateSpace Independent Publishing Platform; Version 2 edition, 2013, Amazon: https://www.amazon.com/dp/1482315823

12. Pressfield, Steven. *Turning Pro: Tap Your Inner Power and Create Your Life's Work*, Black Irish Entertainment LLC, unknown edition, 2012, Amazon: https://www.amazon.com/dp/1936891034

13. Walsch, Neale Donald, Discussion Group based on his book series, *Conversations with God,* available on Amazon and other book outlets

14. Dispenza, Joe. *Becoming Supernatural: How Common People Are Doing the Uncommon*, Hay House Inc, 2nd edition, 2019, Amazon: https://www.amazon.com/dp/1401953115

15. Phillips, Kelle. BlueGrid® Meditation Method, https://inner-communications.teachable.com/p/bluegrid-method

16. Rubinstein, Laura. Founder of https://www.ReEnergizeNow.com

17. Walters, Orna and Matthew. Founders of Creating Love On Purpose and the GPS for Your Soul System. https://www.LoveOnPurpose.com, http://gpsforyoursoul.com

18. Merkley, Christina. Founder of the Shift-It School and creator of the Shift-It System, https://www.shift-it-coach.com

19. Sophia, Jumana. *Break the Grip of Past Lovers: Reclaim Your Personal Power, Recover from Neglect, Manipulations, or Betrayal,*

Reawaken Your Emotional Intimacy (A Book for Women), Hierophant Publishing, 2019, Amazon: https://www.amazon.com/dp/1938289951

20. DailyOM. Website that features a universal approach to holistic living for mind, body, and spirit and supports people who want to live a conscious lifestyle, https://www.dailyom.com

21. Emoto, Dr. Masaru. A pioneer in the study of water.

22. Oregon Health and Science University (OHSU) is a public research university focusing primarily on health sciences with a main campus, including two hospitals, in Portland, Oregon. https://www.ohsu.edu

23. Oregon Ear, Nose & Throat Center. Otolaryngologist in Medford, Oregon. https://oregonent.com/?utm_source=GMBlisting&utm_medium=organic

24. Choquette, Sonia. Divine Energy Oracle cards. https://soniachoquette.net

25. Kondo, Marie. *The Life-Changing Magic of Tidying Up: The Japanese Art of Decluttering and Organizing*, Ten Speed Press; 1st edition, 2014, Amazon: https://www.amazon.com/dp/1607747308

26. Hough, Jennifer. *UNSTUCK: The Physics of Getting Out of Your Own Way*, I Fly Publishing, 1st edition, 2022, Amazon: https://www.amazon.com/dp/B09RWCMDMR

27. Grout, Pam. *E-Squared: Nine Do-It-Self Energy Experiments that Prove Your Thoughts Create Your Reality*, Amazon: https://www.amazon.com/dp/1401938906

28. Campion, Lisa. *Energy Healing for Empaths: How to Protect Yourself from Energy Vampires, Honor Your Boundaries, and Build Healthier Relationships*, Reveal Press, 1st edition, 2021, Amazon: https://www.amazon.com/dp/1684035929

29. PubMed.gov. PubMed® comprises more than 34 million citations for biomedical literature from MEDLINE, life science journals, and online books. Citations may include links to full text content

from PubMed Central and publisher web sites. https://pubmed.
ncbi.nlm.nih.gov

30. Biggs, Kalawana. Healing the Body, Mind and Spirit
    Guided Meditation, YouTube, 2012, https://bit.ly/
    HealingBodyMindSpirit

31. Ianthe Mauro of Objects With Purpose, Creator of the wearable
    candle made with organic coconut butter wax, https://
    objectswithpurpose.com

32. PostHope.org. A free support website to journal your story,
    fundraise and rally patient support.

33. PsychGuides.com. Information for the identification of symptoms
    and signs of psychological disorders, and effective treatment
    and recovery. Guides contain expert consensus guidelines for
    treatments and resources including relevant studies. https://
    www.psychguides.com

34. Mitchell, H.H. Journal of Biological Chemistry 158 Article, "The
    Chemical Composition of the Adult Human Body and Its Bearing
    on the Biochemistry of Growth, https://www.sciencedirect.com/
    science/article/pii/S0021925819513394

35. Social Care Institute for Excellence, Types and Indicators
    of Abuse, https://www.scie.org.uk/safeguarding/adults/
    introduction/types-and-indicators-of-abuse

36. MADHAV University, The Spiritual Consequences of Alcohol
    Consumption, https://madhavuniversity.edu.in/spiritual-
    consequences-of-alcohal-consumption.html?fbclid=IwAR0O-3VU
    1XSgCYScdNy5ftkSYL4cirldj9OtpTgwEtAq9BSBX5k8YZFFOwU

37. Daniel Austin Sperry, Cellist, composer, singer, songwriter, poet,
    spoken-word artist, street musician and community artist, living
    in Ashland, Oregon, https://www.danielaustinsperry.com/

38. Massage, 5 Different Types of Massage Therapies
    and Their Benefits, https://www.closingthegap.
    ca/5-different-types-of-massage-therapies-and-their-benefits/

39. Epsom Salt Baths, Why Take an Epsom Salts Bath?, https://
    www.webmd.com/a-to-z-guides/epsom-salt-bath

40. The Chakra System, The 7 Chakras for Beginners, https://www. mindbodygreen.com/0-91/The-7-Chakras-for-Beginners.html

41. Carne, Sharon of Sound Wellness. Sound Wellness is a holistic modality that uses techniques based on sound and music to bring the body, mind, emotions and spirit back into harmony, https://bit.ly/SoundWellnessStore

42. Eden, Donna of Eden Energy Medicine. Energy Medicine has been called the "Gray's Anatomy of the subtle body." https://www.edenenergymedicine.com

43. Paladino, Tom of Scalar Light™. Scalar Energy is Scalar Light emitted continuously from the Sun of our Solar System, and all the Stars in the Universe. https://www.miraclebalance.net/the-science-behind-scalar-energy/ https://www.scalarlight.com/what-is-scalar-energy

44. Ananda, Nicole Doherty, Healer, Coach, Channeler and Teacher, https://www.nicoledoherty.com

45. Emotional Freedom Technique (EFT), EFT Tapping, https://www.healthline.com/health/eft-tapping#treatment

46. Vitale, Dr. Joe. *The Miracle: Six Steps to Enlightenment*, CreateSpace Independent Publishing Platform, 1st edition, 2016, Amazon: https://www.amazon.com/dp/153689155X

47. ProtectWhiteSage, Instagram, Source to find best practices of white sage and to protect the plants. https://www.instagram.com/protectwhitesage/

48. doTERRA is a manufacturer of high-quality essential oils. https://www.doterra.com/US/en/site/lisamanyon

49. Claire, Em, American Poet and wife of Neale Donald Walsch. https://emclairepoet.love/

50. Cameron, Julia. *The Artist's Way: A Spiritual Path to Higher Creativity*, Souvenir Press, Main edition, 2020, Amazon: https://www.amazon.com/Artists-Way-25th-Anniversary/dp/0143129252

Made in the USA
Las Vegas, NV
18 December 2022

63370114R00125